MW00574223

ONE LIFE, MANY DEATHS

ONE LIFE, MANY DEATHS

A SURGEON'S STORIES

By
H. BROWNELL WHEELER, MD

meredith winter press

Copyright © 2014 by H. Brownell Wheeler

All rights reserved. Published in the United States by

Meredith Winter Press, Cambridge, Massachusetts.

Library of Congress Control Number: 2014914308

ISBN 978-0-692-26936-7

To Betty

CONTENTS

—

INTRODUCTION

—

In February of 1996, I stepped down as chief of surgery at University of Massachusetts Medical Center. At 66, I thought it was time to let a younger surgeon take over. But I had no desire to spend the rest of my life at a golf course, tennis court, or bridge table. Even if I was no longer doing surgery or supervising other surgeons, I still wanted to use the know-how of a lifetime in medical care to help patients. How could I use that knowledge? What clinical problem could I help solve? For a long time, nothing came to mind.

One day, it occurred to me that the greatest suffering I had seen in my career was in dying patients: patients for whom surgery had little to offer—in fact, all of medical science and technology had little to offer. Many, many times I had seen patients in the surgical intensive care unit die slowly and painfully, totally dehumanized, barely recognizable as people. Their images haunted me. Usually, these patients were comatose and on a respirator. Their faces were often bloated, and their eyes swollen shut from futile and overly aggressive use of intravenous fluids. Their arms were covered with blue-purple bruises from intravenous infusions and needle punctures to draw blood. Plastic tubes went through the nose into the stomach for feeding and into the bladder for collecting urine. Often, family members stood nearby with tears in their eyes, barely able to recognize their loved ones and totally unable to communicate with them. I have often thought to myself: *No one should die like this!*

Somehow we ought to have provided a kinder, more humane death for this patient and this family.

I have also seen "good deaths." Deaths that occurred in a quiet room with a loved one holding the patient's hand. Deaths that were peaceful and free of pain. Deaths with the support of caring family members, friends, spiritual counselors, and health-care personnel. Deaths that were a comfort to the survivors, even an inspiration. Deaths that seemed natural, even welcome.

Over 35 years, I had been the chief of surgery at three different hospitals: first, a Veterans Administration hospital; then, a large Catholic community hospital; and finally, a major academic medical center. It was part of my job to review the surgical deaths in those hospitals. I also consulted on many patients facing death and helped them decide among treatment options. I mediated disputes among physicians, nurses, patients, and especially family members, about when to "let go" and when to go "all out" with heroic attempts to save a patient's life. Over a long career, I learned a lot from dying patients, not just about their medical conditions, but also about their personal lives.

Caring for patients with life-threatening conditions taught me that, although the pain of loss is inevitable, much other suffering can be made easier. Some can be totally prevented. With planning by the patient and family, and with support from a competent health-care team, the horror scenes I have witnessed in the Intensive Care Unit (ICU) can usually be prevented. Good deaths can often be achieved. And so, I decided to devote the last phase of my career to improving the care of dying patients.

To prepare myself for this new role, I visited centers of excellence in end-of-life care, and I talked to national leaders in the field. They were generous in sharing their experience and advice. Some became friends. I attended palliative care conferences and read the relevant medical literature. I went on home visits with hospice nurses as they cared for dying patients. Those hospice patients and their caregivers were some of my best teachers. They were often surprised and pleased to have an older physician come to their home and show an interest in their care. They were happy to share what had been helpful to them and to say what had been needed but lacking.

Somewhere along the line, I am not exactly sure when or where or how, I lost my fear of death. I learned to regard death as a mystery with many unanswered questions—but a comfortable mystery and, quite likely, a necessary and welcome friend for most of us.

This book tells the stories of my life that have shaped my changing view of death. They are stories that relate to life's big questions. They also suggest how to help ensure a good death when the time comes. I can vouch for the truth of them all. I have been blessed with the ability to recall many details from events that happened long ago, but I am well aware that memory can play tricks on honest and well-meaning people, so I have made a special effort to include only stories that I remember clearly or can verify with others or with my past written records.

This book is in part a candid personal memoir, with a particular focus on experiences related to death. Writing a personal memoir was not my original intention, but I could not describe my most meaningful life experiences without sharing much of myself in the process. I have been remarkably privileged in the richness and breadth of my experiences. The stories of my life have taught me a lot. They have finally brought me to a place of comfort as I head into old age and eventual death, perhaps before too long. I was not always in that comfortable place. It feels good to be there at last. I hope that this book will help my readers to find their own place of comfort with death.

H. Brownell Wheeler, MD
South Portland, Maine
June 20, 2014

The Early Years: Learning About Death

CHAPTER 1

The Dream

—

When I was about five or six years old, a recurrent nightmare haunted my nights. It began peacefully enough: a pleasant schoolyard scene on a sunny spring day. I was with other children about the same age. We were getting on a school bus to go to a state park for a picnic. We were excited and happy and noisy.

In the dream, I got on the bus with my father. He was in charge of the outing and sat up front by the driver. (In fact, my father was the superintendent of schools in Paintsville, a small town in the hills of eastern Kentucky.)

After a long drive, the bus stopped by the roadside so that some kids could disappear into the woods to empty their bladders in privacy. The rest of us stretched our legs, walking down the road and back. Several minutes went by. The time came to drive on. We all got back into the bus. All, that is, except my father, who was nowhere to be seen. The driver told me that he didn't know where my daddy had gone, but that we couldn't leave without him. Instantly, I knew that something terrible had happened. My father would never be late unless he was seriously ill—or badly injured. In my dream, I saw a bloody handkerchief which I recognized as my father's. I knew immediately that he had been killed by some bad men, and that I would never see him again.

Panic seized me. I bolted out of the bus and ran up and down the road, screaming "Daddy!"

At this point in the dream, I always woke up sobbing and ran into my parents' bedroom. My mother would hug me and whisper that it was only a bad dream. My father's warm body in the bed brought even greater reassurance. Comforted but still upset, I would finally fall asleep, and my father would carry me back to my own bed.

I would wake up in the morning, still unsettled by the nightmare. A few days later, I would have the same terrifying dream again. I became afraid to go to sleep.

Slowly, over many months, the dream faded out of my life. But it remains my earliest realization that people die, sometimes suddenly and unexpectedly.

My first real-life experience with mortality was the death of Lizzie, my step-grandmother. My bloodline grandmother, my father's mother, had died of tuberculosis when she was only 28. My father was then age five or six. His younger sister, Vivian, was only two or three.

One of my father's most indelible childhood memories was being roughly shaken awake in the middle of the night by his aunt, his mother's sister, who rushed him into his best Sunday clothes and then took him hurriedly to the downstairs sickroom where his mother lay dying.

Feebly, his mother took his hand in hers. Her hand was cold and pale.

"Arville," she said, faintly, "Arville … be … a … good … boy." And she closed her eyes.

My father was then quickly whisked away to his own bed. The next morning when he came down for breakfast, his mother's bed was empty. The bed linens had been stripped off. He never forgot that night. He retold the story when he was well into his nineties.

A few years after my grandmother's death, my grandfather remarried. My father's stepmother, Lizzie, didn't lavish much love on her newly acquired stepson. She wasn't by nature a warm, affectionate woman; and she had a hard life as a farm wife. She was always working at one chore or another.

When I was about nine, Lizzie developed an abdominal cancer, probably ovarian or colonic, I would now guess. She had a fairly rapid downhill course. The living room was converted to a bedroom, so she could be close to the kitchen and avoid climbing the stairs. Lizzie died there, in that same room where my grandmother Elizabeth died.

I don't remember feeling any great sadness or sense of loss when Lizzie died. But I was certainly impressed that someone whom I knew well, someone hard working, strong, and tough could suddenly and unexpectedly become sick, die, and be lost from my life forever.

I do not remember much about Lizzie's funeral, just sitting in an uncomfortably hot room at the funeral home, fanning myself with a stiff little cardboard fan stapled to a wooden handle. One side of the fan had a rather saccharine and idealized picture of the risen Christ; the other side said Paintsville Funeral Home with an address and phone number and a slogan, which I no longer remember. My uncle Greenville and aunt Vivian ran the Paintsville Funeral Home, so the funeral probably didn't cost my grandfather much. A blessing, since his only income came from selling farm produce door-to-door from a horse-drawn wagon.

The family cemetery near the farmhouse was the natural—and economical—place to bury Lizzie. My grandfather had already buried his first wife in the same cemetery. And perhaps another dozen family members were buried there.

It was quite a struggle to bring Lizzie's coffin to the hilltop cemetery. Behind a horse-drawn wagon, we had to walk across a dirt road, then go 100 yards down a rough path on a steep grassy bank, wade across a shallow creek, and continue a quarter mile up a hillside hay field with a 30-degree grade. The pallbearers, men of the family in unfamiliar dress shirts and some with ties, walked alongside the wagon. The rest of the family and a few friends followed. It was a hot summer day, and I was sweating. So was everyone else.

A short distance beyond the creek, the hill got steeper. From this point on, the pallbearers carried the casket, rather than trust the wagon. Lizzie had been a stout woman. Her body must have weighed a lot, even after her illness. And the wooden casket, probably made of white oak from the farm, must have been quite heavy even when empty.

My uncles and older cousins carrying the coffin were strong farmers, but they quickly became short of breath and red in the face. Sweat rolled off their foreheads, and their best shirts were soon soaked with sweat. It was a long ordeal to reach the top of the hill, where a freshly dug hole waited to swallow the wooden box with Lizzie in it.

I knew the occasion was solemn and important, but I don't remember feeling sad, just hot and uncomfortable. I was glad when the short burial service was over and the coffin lowered into the ground. The pallbearers took turns shoveling dirt into the grave, and the casket was soon covered. People began to walk back down the hill.

Back at the farmhouse, I took off my sweaty Sunday shirt and shorts, pulled on a clean pair of thin summer shorts and read a book on the front porch—a child dutifully seen, but not heard. Lizzie would have approved.

My mother's family members lived halfway across Kentucky, some in the city of Louisville and others in Greensburg, a little country town not unlike Paintsville. From our house, Louisville was an all-day drive, much of it on unpaved roads. So I didn't get to know my mother's family as well as my father's family. But all were important to me.

My maternal grandfather's death, sudden and unexpected at the age of 60, made a big impression on me. I was about 11 at the time I lost Granddaddy Vance. I remember exactly when the call came. It was nearly suppertime. My mother was in the kitchen, and I was helping her. She was frying slices of green apples together with pork chops in a big skillet. The phone was on the wall nearby. She took the call while turning over the apples and meat with a spatula. She said very little, but I knew from her expression that something terrible had happened. My father came to the phone, took the receiver, and said we would drive to Louisville that very night.

Supper was eaten hurriedly. Some quick packing was done, even more hurriedly. We ate supper hurriedly and quickly packed, under an ominous sense of time pressure. From what little my parents said, I knew that my grandfather was desperately ill. He was not dead, but he might die at any time. Perhaps he'd had a heart attack, I was told.

We climbed into our black 1930s-era Plymouth sedan. My six-year-old brother and I sat in the back seat. It was now dark, and we were told to try to sleep. I must have slept, since I remember very little of the long drive. It was just beginning to get light when we drove up to my grandparents' unpretentious gray stucco house in a middle-class neighborhood.

"There's no funeral wreath on the door! Do you think that means he's still alive?" my mother said, grasping at any straw.

"I don't know, honey. Perhaps," my father replied, without much assurance.

In the house, we were met with grim and tear-stained faces. My grandfather had died early in the evening, probably even before we started our desperate ride through the night. My grandmother was inconsolable, obviously unable to deal with practical arrangements, except to nod her head in agreement when some necessary proposal was made, then she would break out in tears again. There were six daughters with a wide range of age and experience; my aunt Nancy, the oldest, seemed to be the one the others turned to for direction in this crisis.

During visiting hours at the funeral parlor, I tried not to look at my grandfather's face, now so pale and still and lifeless. He was lying in his best suit and necktie in an ornate casket surrounded by flowers. It all seemed quite unreal. How could this lifeless figure be the same grandfather who had tried to teach me to swim? I remembered the feel of his strong hands supporting my chest and abdomen while I tried to get my arms and legs to do the breaststroke. Grandfather Vance was a calm and reassuring presence in my life. I had felt more warmth and love from him than from any of my other grandparents. How could Daddy Vance no longer be there? Where was he? I just knew that the grandfather I had known and loved was not in that casket.

Vance Family, 1939: arrows point to me and my grandfather; his sudden death was a great shock. Standing directly behind my grandfather are my father and mother.

I walked out of the funeral parlor with my mother, who held one of my hands, and my grandmother, who held the other. As we were walking down the carpeted steps, a Catholic nun rushed up and grabbed my grandmother's hand. (I have no idea why a Catholic nun was coming to pay her respects to my grandfather, a lifelong Methodist.)

"Oh, Mrs. Vance! I'm so sorry," she said. "I know just how you feel. I lost my mother last year."

This expression of sympathy provoked a fresh round of sobbing. My grandmother wailed loudly, "Losing your mother is nothing like losing a husband!" And there were more sobs.

My mother said something more graceful, thanking the nun for her sympathy and saying that we appreciated her coming. Then she hurried us on quickly. I felt sorry for the nun. She obviously meant well, but my grandmother had rebuffed her rather rudely, I thought. And to me, the loss of a mother seemed like the greatest loss possible. Why should my grandmother think that the loss of her husband was worse than losing a mother?

Over the years since, I have learned not to tell someone grieving, "I know just how you feel." It is much better to simply say how sorry you are for them. I have also learned that losing your mother at an advanced age, after you have long since left home, is indeed not to be compared with losing your longtime spouse suddenly and unexpectedly in midlife.

The next day I fidgeted through the long funeral. I wasn't comforted by the minister's conviction that my grandfather was now in heaven with Jesus and his angels. The whole idea seemed quite unreal, even distasteful. I didn't like his statement that my grandfather's sins had been forgiven because of Jesus' death on the cross. I didn't like to think of my grandfather as a sinner, and I didn't like to think of Jesus dying on the cross.

I fidgeted more as the mourners sang *The Old Rugged Cross*: "On a hill far away, stood an old rugged cross, the emblem of suffering and shame. And I love that old cross …" The more militant strains of *Onward, Christian Soldiers* followed—not my cup of tea, then or now.

Instead, I was just aware of a tremendous void in my heart where my grandfather had been. As nearly as I could understand, he was totally and irrevocably gone, vanished completely, almost as though he had never existed. The grandfather I knew certainly wasn't in the cold, pale, waxy corpse.

Nor did I think he was in the coffin I saw lowered into the ground at the cemetery. Each of us in the family tossed a rose into the grave, then men with shovels rudely covered them over with dirt. The pastor commended the spirit of my grandfather to God and then recited: "Ashes to ashes, dust to dust." The whole thing seemed unreal to me. What was real was the grief of my mother and my grandmother and the fact that my grandfather was gone from me forever. Death seemed to me the end of everything. The loss of a loved one was the greatest tragedy I could imagine.

CHAPTER 2

The Farm

—

You can take a boy out of the country, but you can't take the country out of the boy.
well-known Appalachian aphorism

And it was certainly true of my father. He grew up on a farm, loved it, and talked about it all his life. He felt that a farm life was a healthy life, a life close to nature. He wanted me to have that experience, so he arranged for me to spend school vacations and summers working on my grandfather's farm.

When I first started spending time on the farm, it seemed antiquated and rough. My home in Paintsville was far from luxurious, but at least it had electricity, running water, a furnace, and indoor plumbing. The farm had none of those amenities. Water was hauled up from an outdoor well in a bucket. The house was unheated, except for the kitchen, where there was usually a fire in the big cast-iron stove. The living room had a fireplace, but a fire was not often lit. The rooms were lighted at night by kerosene lamps.

The farm had a hand-crank telephone, but it was rarely used. My grandfather had the phone installed to summon help in case of a fire. It was a party line, with all calls going through a switchboard operator. To make a call, you turned the crank on the side of the phone. That summoned the operator, who then placed the call for you. Each party had its own call sequence, such as two long rings, followed by two short rings. There were special rings for fires and emergencies. If your call sequence rang, you picked up the phone and answered. Before long you learned your neighbors' call sequences as well as your own. If you picked up the phone after their ring, you could listen in on your neighbor's conversation. If you were nosy, you soon knew all the local gossip. So did the switchboard operator.

There were no bathrooms in the house. A two-hole outhouse stood about 50 feet from the kitchen door. I hated the smell of the outhouse. And the flies! Pages torn from an old Montgomery Ward mail-order catalog served as toilet paper. The same catalog also provided reading material during lengthy visits.

Life on the farm seemed uncomfortable and downright inconvenient to me at first. And there were always little chores for me to do: Water had to be brought in from the well several times each day. The garden always needed tending. Chickens needed to be fed and to have their eggs collected. The horse needed fresh hay in its bin, and the pig needed scraps from the table. The kerosene lamps had to be refilled and have their wicks trimmed and their chimneys washed clean of the smoky residue. Old flypaper had to be taken down when it lost its stickiness or became full of dead and dying flies, and new flypaper had to be put up.

I have indelible memories of garden chores, such as planting corn. You started by putting five kernels in each little corn hill. Then in two or three weeks, you thinned the five little stalks to the two best. After another couple of weeks, you pulled out the weaker stalk, leaving only the strongest of the five little stalks that first sprouted. What I remember most, though, is how much my back ached after bending over each corn hill all up and down the long rows. And how it ached after picking long rows of beans, bending over the plants, holding back the leaves with one hand to reveal the bean pods underneath, and picking them off the plant with my other hand. Before long, my back was sore, and I was tired. And I was slow. My stepgrandmother, Lizzie, would sometimes get impatient and come out and take over picking the beans from me. I was embarrassed but glad to see her come.

There were no other children my age, and no games to play. My grandparents did not play cards or any other games that I recall. In the evening or on rainy days or when guests arrived, they would sit on the front porch and talk. It was their primary recreation. Even when sitting on the porch, Lizzie would usually knit or sew. My grandfather would sometimes sit in the swing and chew tobacco. From time to time, he would lean out toward the yard and spit a stream of brown tobacco juice into the grass. I made it a point never to walk near those spots.

The talk of the adults was mostly about the weather and its effect on the crops. Often, they would ponder long-term prospects for the gardens and fields, as well as the health of the livestock. Or they might discuss various members of our large family and their current activities. Sometimes they talked about the neighbors. I do not recall much talk about politics or world affairs or sports. Sometimes, to entertain a guest, my grandfather would tell a story. Mostly, farm talk was boring to me. I would sit on the edge of the porch and whittle the bark off sticks with my jackknife. Sometimes I would take out a bag of marbles I had brought from town and play with them in the driveway.

But other farm activities were far from boring. Some were electrifying, even horrifying. One morning soon after I arrived on the farm, Lizzie said to my grandfather, "Franklin, we need a chicken for supper. Would you fetch me one?" My grandfather nodded his head and motioned for me to follow him. Where were we going? What were we going to do? I was frightened, without knowing why.

My grandfather walked briskly out of the kitchen, through the dining room and the living room, and out the front door. I followed him across the front porch, into the yard, and down the path to the henhouse on the far side of the dirt road that connected our farm with the outside world. When we opened the henhouse door, a cacophony of agitated squawking began. The birds were terrified. They sensed something that I did not.

My grandfather calmly looked from one bird to another, selecting our supper. Then in a sudden motion, his strong, callused hands grabbed the legs of the chosen bird. The chicken struggled mightily to get away, flapping its wings and trying to free its legs from that death grip. But its struggles were useless. My grandfather was just too strong. Years of strenuous work on the farm had given him the heavily muscled hands and arms of a construction worker.

Back in the front yard, my grandfather let one hand loose from the legs in order to grip the upper neck. Suddenly, he released the bird's legs and swung the bird rapidly, round and round his head, holding it only by its neck. The twisting force was too much for the slender neck. To my horror, it tore loose from the head, and the headless bird went running in aimless circles around the yard, flapping its wings. How could it run without a head? What was controlling its frantic movements?

After a few seconds of this erratic behavior, the bloody, headless bird flopped down on the grass and was still—dead at last. My grandfather said calmly, "Take the bird to Lizzie. I have things to do in the barn." And he left me alone with the bird's bloody carcass on the grass.

It took me a long time to pick up that chicken. I felt like an accomplice to a murder. Perhaps this was the same bird I had petted with affection when I collected eggs yesterday. Wringing its neck felt cruel, just plain wrong. But what was I to do? The deed was done. Slowly, with grim determination, I picked up the bird's legs and held the body an arm's length away as I walked to the kitchen.

Lizzie was waiting with a large metal basin and a teakettle full of boiling water. She slit the belly open and scooped out the viscera. Then she put the carcass in the basin and poured hot water over it. She swirled the bird around in the hot water for a minute and then said, "Now help me pluck it." Reluctantly, I pulled out a few wet feathers while Lizzie plucked the rest.

I had seen my first death on the farm. There were many to come: mostly chickens, but occasionally a pig was killed by having its throat cut. Once I heard a gunshot in the barn. I was told that a sick, old horse had to be "put away" with a rifle bullet to the back of the head. I was horrified at killing the horse. It had seemed so big and strong. And it liked to be petted.

I never got used to seeing a farm animal killed. But I once asked my grandfather to kill an enormous blacksnake that lived in our barn. When I had chores there, I was terrified of the snake, even though I had been told blacksnakes were harmless. My grandfather refused my request, saying the snake ate rats and mice that would otherwise do a lot of harm. It was a farmer's friend, he explained. He even called the snake by a pet name, Old Blackie.

Wheeler Family Farmhouse: built 1873-1874 by my great-grandfather,
and a one-armed carpenter who was a casualty of the Civil War

But wanting to kill the snake was an exception. As a child, I never wanted to kill any other animal, not even an insect. I didn't like to swat flies or put up flypaper, which would hold them helpless, buzzing frantically until they died. It just felt wrong to kill any living being. Years later, I learned that many people felt the same way. "Reverence for life" was the basic philosophy of Albert Schweitzer, winner of the Nobel Peace Prize and perhaps the most influential philosopher of the early 20th century. "No killing" is one of the Buddha's five basic precepts and a tenet followed by perhaps a billion people. Still, on my grandfather's farm, not killing animals seemed like an impossible way to live. We raised them to be killed and eaten. But the killing was hard for me to accept.

CHAPTER 3

The Ghost

—

Rural Appalachia in the early 20th century was a place of poverty, limited educational opportunities, and fundamentalist Christian beliefs. Superstition was common. Many farm families had supernatural tales to tell. Most were easy to dismiss. However, there were tales in my own family, told by people I respected and was sure were honest—like my father. It was not so easy to dismiss his stories. One of the stories that came down through my family was a ghost story set on our family farm. I had trouble believing it was just a fantasy.

Lora Alice was my grandfather's older sister. She was a reliable worker on the farm, spending many hours in the fields and seeming to enjoy the hard outdoor life. She was a particular favorite of her mother, Sarah, who had 11 children but "set special store by Lora Alice," as family members said.

One day Lora Alice was working with the men, harvesting wheat on the same hillside where years later Lizzie's casket would be carried up with such difficulty. On that hot late-summer day, the crest of the hill was a peaceful place, shaded by oaks and maples. Lora Alice and the men working with her decided to take a break in the shade of the trees. Lying there, they saw the whole farm laid out below: the two-story white frame house, built by my great-grandfather; the well beside the house; the outhouse in back; the grassy front yard with its hen-house by the road; the kitchen garden on the south side of the house and the large vegetable gardens on either side. They saw the large, gray barn and behind it a pig-pen, a few cows, a horse, a mule, and pastures. They saw the dark woods covering the hill behind the farm and the dusty dirt road winding in front of the house, following the creek bed around the bend to the next farm. It was a tranquil and picturesque and familiar scene.

"Isn't it just beautiful up here?" Lora Alice was later remembered to have said. "It's so peaceful!"

After a few moments, Lora Alice spoke again, "It's so peaceful here. ... When I die, this place is where I want to be buried. ... I could just look at this scene for-ever."

"Let's get back to work," one of the men said abruptly. There was work to be done. No time for a young woman's thoughts about the view, especially depressing thoughts about where to be buried. Lora Alice was still a teen-age girl, strong and healthy, why would she talk like that?

Late summer was followed by an early fall. It was the fall of an influenza epidemic. One week Lora Alice was strong and healthy. A week later, she was dead. And the men remembered. They worked out their grief and anger and frustration at her early death by digging a grave on the hilltop she had found so peaceful. Perhaps, they thought, she might really look down forever at the farm she loved so much.

Other family members were buried there later. They included my grandmother, who died of TB. But resting in the shade of a grove of trees on a hilltop overlooking the farm is not the end of Lora Alice's story. In my family lore, that is just the start of a ghost story that was told to me, perhaps too many times, by my father.

After Lora Alice's death—so rapid and unexpected in the prime of her life—her mother, Sarah, was inconsolable. The most helpful, most loving, most good-natured child, Lora Alice was to have been the comfort and support of her mother in time to come in her old age. Her daughter's unexpected early death was too much for Sarah to bear.

To compound her grief, my great-grandmother kept feeling that Lora Alice was not really dead, that her spirit was in fact very much alive and present in the farmhouse. Lora Alice was a constant presence to her mother: nearby, but invisible, and anxious to communicate.

Lora Alice's father, Martin Van Buren Wheeler, was a stern, taciturn man. Stiff upper lip, unemotional. He never let out his feelings, and he felt his wife should behave in the same way. He felt that she was irrational, made semi-crazy by her grief. If Martin shared Sarah's sense of loss, he never let on to anyone else.

One day the grief-stricken mother was baking in the kitchen. More specifically, as I recall the story, Sarah was making an apple pie, filling a pastry shell with cut-up pieces of apple. She suddenly felt Lora Alice's presence behind her. It was an unusually powerful feeling. There was no doubt: Lora Alice was standing behind her! Then she felt Lora Alice's hand on her shoulder. "Lora Alice!!" she cried out and whirled around to see her daughter. But Lora Alice was nowhere to be seen. Sarah collapsed in tears.

On another occasion, Sarah was picking beans in the garden. During the whole morning, she had felt that Lora Alice was near her, wanting desperately to tell her something. Bending over the bean plants, lifting the leaves to see the green beans hiding underneath, she again felt Lora Alice's hand on her shoulder. Quickly, she looked up. Once again, there was no one to be seen.

Sarah was convinced by these experiences, and others, that Lora Alice's spirit was now roaming the house as a ghost—a troubled ghost who wanted very much to talk to her mother. And Sarah wanted very much to talk to Lora Alice.

Seventy miles away—far beyond the little creek that ran by our farm; beyond the larger Paint Creek, into which our little creek ran; beyond the Big Sandy River, into which Paint Creek ran, and which was the state line dividing Kentucky from West Virginia—there lived a medium who was reputed to be able to summon spirits of the dead and to let their voices speak through her body. Tales of her séances were told in hushed tones throughout the region. Many observers were convinced of her honesty. Some thought her psychic powers were gifts of God. Others hinted darkly that they were not gifts of God, but gifts of the devil. And some simply thought she was a fraud and a charlatan, albeit an extremely clever one. In a poor rural area that lacked much drama in everyday life, the medium was a titillating source of gossip and conjecture, mainly whispered about by the women and ignored by the men.

Some of the women urged Sarah to go see the medium, but that was not an easy matter. Seventy miles was a long way over dirt roads in a horse-drawn farm wagon. And like most other men in the hills of eastern Kentucky in the 1930s, my great-grandfather had no faith in any medium and no desire to make the trip. He scorned any presumed psychic or occult communications, and he stressed the time and effort and cost of such a wild goose chase.

But Sarah kept begging, often with tears in her eyes. Finally, Martin relented. They packed for the trip, hitched up the horse and wagon, and began the long, slow journey to West Virginia. Martin was glum. Sarah was excited and hopeful but also apprehensive. She didn't know what to expect. But she hoped to talk to Lora Alice. Eventually, after a long, dusty trip, they were able to find the medium and arrange a séance.

That séance always remained vivid in Sarah's memory. It must have remained vivid in Martin's memory too, but he would never talk about it. He also forbade anyone else in the family from talking about it, which pretty much ensured that it would be discussed often, but in hushed tones out of Martin's earshot. My father heard the story many times as a child, directly from Sarah, and he duly passed it down through our family.

According to Sarah, the séance began late one evening in a darkened room. The wicks of the kerosene lamps were turned down until only a tiny flame remained. The medium, a middle-aged woman, closed her eyes, took several deep breaths, and seemed to almost stop breathing. Sarah saw, or imagined, tiny sparks of light flying around the dark room. It seemed to Sarah that the room was filled with unseen spirits. The medium's eyes remained closed. She seemed to be in some sort of trance-like state. So it came as a surprise when she suddenly spoke to Sarah, but in a different voice and with a different manner of speech. The voice purported to be that of Sarah's long-dead nephew, her sister's son David. He had died of diphtheria when he was about three years old.

Don't cry for us, Aunt Sarah. We're happy here. It's beautiful. You'll see some day.

Sarah didn't know what to think or how to react. *How can I be sure it's really you, David? You couldn't talk too well before you died. How come you talk so well now?*

It's me, all right. We go on growing up here, Aunt Sarah. I'm not just like I used to be. I'm as old as I would be if I were still with you. I'd like to talk to you more, but Lora Alice is here and she is anxious to talk to you.

The medium shifted her position in the chair, but her eyes remained closed and she seemed even deeper in her trance. After a moment, she spoke again, but the voice and the manner were different. The voice was that of Lora Alice. Sarah was sure of it.

Mother, please don't take my death so hard. I have hated so much to see you cry. It's just like David says, it's beautiful here. I'm happy to be here. But I hate to see you cry. I've tried so hard to tell you that I'm happy and that I look forward to seeing you again. Soon. Time goes so fast here! I know you've felt me near, but you could never see me. That has been hard for me, as well as you. I'm so glad you're here and I can talk to you now.

"Oh, Lora Alice. It sounds so much like you! I want so much to believe it's you! But I still can't see you. How can I be sure that it's really you talking to me?" Sarah said.

Your heart knows. Trust your heart. Remember when you were cutting up apples for a pie back in the kitchen at the farm. I tried so hard to reach you. I summoned all my energy and made you feel my hand on your shoulder. You knew it was me all right, even if you couldn't see me. And you surely remember too how hard I tried to reach you when you were picking beans in the garden. Once again, I drew on all my strength and made you feel my touch. You knew it was me, even if you couldn't see me when you turned around.

There were other times when Sarah had felt Lora Alice's presence, which the voice speaking through the medium was able to describe in detail. Sarah was completely convinced. There was no way for the medium to know about the pie making or the bean picking. Or other events recalled accurately and in great detail. Besides, just as Lora Alice said, Sarah's heart knew and was comforted at last.

The long wagon ride back to the farm was spent in silence, except for the rhythmic clip-clop of the horse's hoofs on the dirt road. Sarah was finally at peace. The trip had confirmed her belief that Lora Alice had been trying to speak to her. Now she also felt sure that the spirit of Lora Alice was alive and well, although somewhere beyond her sight or reach. "In heaven," her Southern Baptist minister would surely say. To be honest, Sarah had never been so sure there was a heaven—until now.

Sarah was finally at peace, but Martin was now consumed with turbulent emotions. He had seen and heard what Sarah saw and heard. But he was not as able as she to accept that the voice they heard was truly that of Lora Alice. He still could not believe in ghosts or mediums. But he was perplexed. How could the medium so successfully mimic the voice of someone she never knew? How could she know about the times when Sarah had felt that Lora Alice was close beside her in the kitchen or the garden? With a troubled mind, he pondered the events that challenged his strong beliefs. Gradually, he came to a frightening conclusion: This must be the work of the devil!

Wheeler Family Reunion at the old famhouse, 1910

To Martin and his Southern Baptist brethren, the devil was a real and present danger, ever active on the human stage. Good Christians must always beware his presence. Fiery sermons had been preached on the subject: Look for him everywhere. Don't be tempted or beguiled by disguises. Don't believe what he says through others' lips. These thoughts troubled Martin greatly. So he sternly admonished Sarah to say nothing of their trip to anyone. And he himself never spoke of the trip, except to say darkly that the medium could not be trusted. She was surely in league with the devil.

This forbidden secret about the séance was too intriguing for Sarah not to share with her other children. After all, they were Lora Alice's sisters and brothers. When they pressed her for details of what happened on the long trip to West Virginia and back, she would say in a hushed voice, *Well, don't tell your father, but* . . . and the story would come out, with many questions and all the details. And in time the story would be passed down to Sarah's grandchildren, Lora Alice's nieces and nephews.

My father was Lora Alice's nephew. He heard the story from Sarah herself. My father was a favorite grandchild. We lived near Sarah after Martin died and she left the farm for a tiny house in town. Every year for Christmas, my father would give Sarah a large can of Prince Albert smoking tobacco. In warm weather she loved to sit in a straight-back rocking chair on her small front porch and smoke her corncob pipe. Perhaps smoking wasn't good for her, but she died at the age of 97. I remember her as being alert at 95 and the focus of many large family reunions.

I have visited Lora Alice's grave with its small headstone on the hilltop. I have stood in the farmhouse kitchen and in the vegetable garden where Sarah's visitations occurred. Lora Alice has never made an effort to communicate with me. But then I didn't expect she would. Hopefully, she has better things to do. I like to think that she may be laughing with Sarah about my telling their story so many years later. Perhaps even Martin is laughing.

And perhaps it is just a fanciful tale of superstitious farm folks, much embellished in the retelling. Whatever the real explanation, it opened my young mind up to the possibility that someone's spirit might survive death ... but how? ... and where?

CHAPTER 4

Family Stories

—

When I was growing up, the story of Lora Alice and other strange stories in our family fascinated me. Several involved my father. I believed all of them because I could not imagine my father telling me something that wasn't true. One such story was about a vivid and prophetic dream in his late teens. It impressed me because my father was telling me something that he had experienced personally, not something described to him secondhand.

When my father was growing up, there was no high school anywhere near the family farm. When he reached high school age, he was sent to Paintsville. He stayed with his uncle John, a lawyer and local judge. Uncle John lived in a big white frame house with a wraparound front porch and a couple of spare bedrooms. He offered free room and board so that my father could get a high-school education. In return, my grandfather provided his older brother with fresh farm produce delivered to his home in a horse-drawn wagon every Thursday.

One night at Uncle John's, my father had an unusually vivid dream. In the dream, he was returning to Uncle John's house. He went up the front steps, crossed the front porch, and opened the door into the living room. The furniture had been moved away from one wall.

Where a couch had been, there was a coffin, its bottom half covered by an American flag. There were sprays of funeral flowers on the floor by the casket. My father knew instinctively that there was a corpse in the casket, even though it was closed. But who was dead? Why was the coffin in Uncle John's living room? The scene was so vivid, so real, that my father woke up in a cold sweat, sure beyond any doubt that someone in the house had died. He jumped out of bed and ran down the hall to Uncle John's room.

"Uncle John," he cried out. "Who has died?"

Uncle John awoke with a start. "What the hell are you talking about?" He was angry at being wakened with such a start in the middle of the night. Uncle John was a tall, stern, rather dour man whose face was rarely creased by a smile. Defendants in his courtroom must have cringed at his gaze. I can imagine my father suddenly realizing how silly he must seem to his stern uncle as he tried to explain about the dream. And how foolish he must have felt as he went back down the dark corridor to his bedroom. But the dream was so unusual and so vivid that he was convinced it must have some hidden meaning. The images remained with him for the rest of his life. And the meaning became clear later on.

After finishing high school, my father worked his way through Centre College, a small school in the middle of the state. During one break his first year, he came back to visit his family in eastern Kentucky. On the way, he stopped to see Uncle John. He walked up the wide front steps, crossed the porch, and opened the door into the living room. In front of him, where a couch had been, was a flag-draped casket, surrounded by sprays of funeral flowers. It was the exact scene he had seen in his dream many months before.

Who in the house has died? he thought and called out, "Uncle John … Aunt Douglas. It's Arville."

After a moment Uncle John appeared and explained what had happened. Nobody in our family had died. He and Aunt Douglas had decided to rent out a room to a boarder, a nice young man who worked for the railroad. The man had no family that they knew of, certainly not in our region. His background was a bit of a mystery. He had been a soldier in World War I. After the war, which he never talked about, he got a job with the Chesapeake & Ohio Railroad and was assigned to the freight yard and station house in Paintsville. One day there was an accident at the rail yard. Uncle John wasn't clear exactly how it had happened, but somehow the young man had been crushed to death between two railcars.

No one at the railroad station knew if the man had a family elsewhere or, if so, how to contact them. Nevertheless, my Uncle John and the man's co-workers all agreed that he must have a Christian funeral. The local veterans' organization provided an American flag and a casket, and the railroad covered the other basic expenses. Uncle John agreed to hold the wake and funeral service in his home. As far as was known, Uncle John's house was the only home the man had. He was buried in Paintsville.

So the scene my father encountered on his return to the house was explained. What was never explained, though, was how he had seen the same scene in a dream long before the actual event. He always was intrigued by those circumstances, but he never came up with any explanation. Unknown to my father, the famous Swiss psychiatrist Carl Jung had described premonitory dreams in detail, both his own dreams and those of others. Often the dreams were related to an impending death. Jung called them "precognitive" dreams.

Other members of my family had their own stories of psychic or paranormal experiences. Tales told by my uncle Banky—my grandfather's older brother, Casabianca Wheeler, the only person of that unusual name that I ever knew—especially impressed me. Banky was an old-fashioned country doctor who rode his horse on house calls in the country—the saddlebags bulging with bandages, pills, simple surgical instruments, and syringes. I was in awe of him as a young child, but I only saw him a few times at family gatherings. Perhaps he was just too busy or too old or too sick, but he was only occasionally at family reunions. He died while I was still a teenager.

The story I remember best from Uncle Banky had to do with a night when he was called to see a desperately sick child who lived on a farm several miles away. The child had diphtheria, a fearsome and often fatal disease of children in those days. Often, a thick gray membrane would coat the throat. The thicker the membrane became, the less room there was for air to pass, especially in small children with small airways. Then breathing became agonized, and the child made obstructed, crowing sounds. Sometimes a country doctor could reach a finger down far into the struggling child's throat and strip out the gray diphtheritic membrane, allowing the child to breathe more freely, at least for a time. Sometimes this desperate maneuver was enough to save the child's life.

After getting the urgent call that the child could

hardly breathe, Uncle Banky rode his horse as fast as he dared in the dark. He knew that the child's life might depend on getting there in time to strip out the membrane obstructing the airway. Suddenly, the horse reared up with a terrified whinny. Directly ahead, Uncle Banky saw a poorly defined white form by the side of the road. It looked like a small figure threshing about frantically. Obviously, the horse saw the same apparition and was badly frightened by it. Uncle Banky was afraid that the horse might bolt. He jumped off the horse quickly and held the animal's head, spoke to him soothingly, and tried to calm him down. Whatever they had both seen, it disappeared as quickly as it had appeared. But the horse had been spooked badly. It was several minutes before Uncle Banky dared to ride him again. Frustrated and well aware of the importance of time to the sick child, he pulled out his gold pocket watch and noted the time. A few minutes later, when the horse had calmed down, they finally resumed their journey. When they arrived at the child's home, the whole family was gathered around the bedside. The child had died.

"We sure do appreciate your coming all this way, Doc, but you're too late. Johnny just couldn't get his breath. He had a convulsion. He died before you could get here."

"How long ago did he die?"

"On the stroke of 11."

Eleven o'clock was the exact time Uncle Banky had noted on his watch just a moment after he—and his horse—saw a ghostly small figure writhing on the ground by the side of the road.

This story always intrigued me. As a child, I

doubted the existence of ghosts or spirits. I doubted anything supernatural. I even doubted Bible stories. They just seemed hard to believe. But this story of Uncle Banky seemed to me to have the ring of truth. For one thing, I was impressed that the horse saw something extraordinary and frightening. I thought that animals were less apt to imagine things than people. Also, the fact that the apparition occurred at the exact moment of the child's death seemed too much of a coincidence to be due to chance. And I couldn't believe that Uncle Banky would make up the story. He was a sober, unemotional man who seemed quite unlikely to fantasize or fabricate. The whole family came from a hellfire-and-damnation Southern Baptist background, including some preachers. Telling a lie, even a white lie or a fib to amuse children, would have been a sinful act. It just wasn't in their makeup.

My father, about 1980: teller of family ghost stories and premonitory dreams

So I trusted my own family when they experienced something firsthand. Lying was a sin. My father, who had switched to the more liberal Methodist church, could not have told a lie if he tried. So the story of his precognitive dream seemed quite credible, although I had no idea how to explain it. Uncle Banky would never have lied about seeing a child's ghost by the roadside, as witnessed also by his horse. Great-Grandmother Sarah would never have made up her story about Lora Alice, especially about begging her husband to take a long wagon trip to see a medium. So I believed those stories, although I doubted many others.

I became preoccupied with the thought of death, the thought that everyone must die: my mother, my father, my younger brother ... and me. Especially me! And that death is always somewhere near, perhaps waiting just around the corner. I remembered that I had been quite sick with pneumonia as a six-year-old. I realized for the first time that I could well have died from that illness—or from the ruptured appendix I had at about the same age. There were no antibiotics in those days.

About this time, I got interested in becoming a doctor. I fantasized how wonderful it would be to start a hospital where no patient ever died. Where anyone who fell ill—like my father's mother, Elizabeth, with TB or his aunt Lora Alice with influenza or my grandfather Vance with a heart attack—could all be cared for, with the absolute assurance that they would get well and never, ever, die. It was many years before I realized what a nightmare that would be.

As a child, I did not know what to think about stories of the supernatural. So I tried not to think about them at all. Mysteries made me uncomfortable.

CHAPTER 5

The Sick Child

—

In the 1930s, infectious diseases were the leading cause of death in children. Diseases due to pneumococci, streptococci, staphylococci, and other bacteria—now so easily treated with antibiotics—were then a parent's worst nightmare. My own parents became quite alarmed when, at the age of 6, I developed a high fever and racking cough. They were shocked and frightened when our family doctor told them that my chest X-ray showed lobar pneumonia and my sputum showed pneumococci under the microscope. The mortality rate of lobar pneumonia due to the pneumococcus was 30 percent. Dr. Hall said that I would have to be hospitalized immediately.

I was in the Paintsville community hospital for a long time, but I remember very little about it: perhaps because I was so young, perhaps because I was so sick, perhaps simply because it was such a long time ago. The one clear memory that I can dredge up now is a visit from Mr. Robert Montgomery, the high-school basketball coach. Basketball was a big deal in Paintsville, even to a child. A personal visit from the coach was a truly memorable event in my life.

Coach Montgomery gave me a model airplane he had built. He also brought a child size shirt and shorts for the Paintsville Tigers basketball team. The uniform had blue letters on a white background, the player number five, and the word Tigers written prominently on the shirt and shorts. He told me that when I got well, I could be the team mascot and shoot the ball with the team during the pre-game warm-up and the halftime intermission. It was a powerful incentive to get well! (And it really happened, at least once. After I recovered, one night I wore my No. 5 Tigers uniform and came out on the basketball court at the half. But it didn't work out as I had dreamed it would. The ball felt like it weighed 1,000 pounds! I couldn't begin to get it up to the basket! I was embarrassed and felt out of place. I never went out on the basketball court again. The uniform just sat unused on a shelf in my closet, but it had served its purpose.)

When I finally left the hospital, I must have looked like a pathetic little invalid. I needed a caregiver to look after me at home. My mother resigned her teaching job to nurse me back to health. She spent most of her time as my private tutor, teaching me the subjects that I was missing in school. Before long, we had gone far beyond what I had missed and into course material from later grades.

My father did his part in my home schooling, chiefly by encouraging me to read. One strong incentive that he provided was a five-cent reward for every book I read. A nickel was a big deal in my life then. For a nickel I could get a candy bar. Maybe a Hershey bar or a Baby Ruth or a Milky Way or a Mounds bar. My father's rewards may not have been good for my teeth, but they were a powerful stimulus to read. I ended up with over 100 books on my reading list.

When I finally went back to first grade many

weeks later, I was so far ahead of my classmates that I was transferred to the second grade. There too I was well ahead of the class. By the end of the school year, I was promoted to the fourth grade, two full years ahead of schedule. It was a mixed blessing. The schoolwork was no problem. My mother had prepared me well. But my social skills and sports performance were well behind my older classmates. I was often the last one to be selected when choosing up sides for a softball game. I felt inadequate and unwanted.

But when it came to schoolwork, I stayed well ahead of my older classmates. My mother had tutored me in a way that made learning seem like fun. I even liked to take tests. They seemed like doing a crossword puzzle or some mind game. I did well in school and developed increasing self-confidence. I doubt if I would have done as well if I had not had a life-threatening illness that led my mother to give up her teaching job to care for me. The best teacher in my school became my private tutor. With this head start, it was easy to stay ranked among the best students right up through high school.

My senior year in high school, a competitive examination was sponsored by Vanderbilt University for high-school students on the college track. The winners received a Founder's Scholarship, which provided free tuition to Vanderbilt. To my surprise, I was one of the winners. I didn't know much about Vanderbilt, but my father said it was one of the best colleges in the South—and the free tuition was a godsend to our family. There was no question as to where I would go to college. I did not apply to any other college.

Vanderbilt had an accelerated pre-med program for

able students. The medical school agreed to accept Vanderbilt pre-med students who were doing well in their studies after only three years of college. Usually, four years of college were required. At the end of the first year of medical school, students in the accelerated program received a bachelor's degree. The first year of medical school was credited as the fourth year of college. After a total of seven years, students in the accelerated program received both BA and MD degrees from Vanderbilt. It saved time and money. I was glad when I was accepted to medical school in the accelerated program. I was quite content with Vanderbilt.

The Vanderbilt Unversity Campus was breathtaking to a 16-year-old freshman from Eastern Kentucky.

My father was not so sure, however. He had a first cousin, Edward Wheeler Dempsey, who was on the faculty of Harvard Medical School. Without my knowledge, my father wrote Ed Dempsey and asked him if Vanderbilt was a good medical school and if he thought it was a good place for me. The answer came back: Yes, Vanderbilt has a good medical school, but a handful of others might be even better. Harvard led Ed Dempsey's short list of other recommendations. My father asked me to apply to them all. I did not want to fill out any more application forms, and I was quite satisfied with Vanderbilt. Finally, I agreed to apply just to Harvard in order to satisfy my father. I thought that there wasn't any reasonable possibility that I would be accepted after only three years at Vanderbilt, when I would be competing against many applicants with more preparation, some with MS or PhD degrees. Besides, I was only 18 years old when I applied. What chance did I have against these older and much better prepared applicants?

Edward Wheeler Dempsey, PhD, Associate Professor of Anatomy at Harvard Medical School: my father's first cousin and the reason I went to Harvard
Credit: Aesculapiad (Harvard Medical School Yearbook 1952)

So it came as a great shock when I got a letter of acceptance from Harvard Medical School. I had not even had an interview! And I really did not want to go to Harvard. I considered it an elitist school. And I secretly wondered if I could really compete. Vanderbilt seemed comfortable. Harvard seemed risky. But everyone I talked to advised me to go to Harvard, especially my father. And so I went there.

When I finished my medical training in Boston, I remained on the faculty. Harvard was my gateway to a gratifying career. Perhaps Vanderbilt would have been too. And neither of them would have been possible without the boost I got from home tutoring during my long recovery from a life-threatening illness. That academic jump-start was the silver lining to a dark cloud. It set the stage for my professional career.

CHAPTER 6

My Roommate Is Killed in Korea

—

The class of 1952 at Harvard Medical School was full of high achievers. Some had remarkable family backgrounds as well. Charles Huggins, the father of one classmate, was a Nobel Laureate in Medicine. Another classmate's father, Linus Pauling, won two Nobel Prizes, one in medicine and the other in peace. The mother of still another classmate was a reigning diva at the Metropolitan Opera. Some of my classmates had PhD degrees and substantial research accomplishments of their own. Even those who seemed least impressive on first meeting often turned out to have remarkable backgrounds on closer acquaintance. Unless you got to know them really well, you might never suspect their distinctions—except for the fact that they had all been chosen for a highly coveted place at one of Harvard's most competitive graduate schools. Such an easily overlooked person was Peter Kelemen.

About 120 medical students entered the class of 1952, many of whom I barely got to know. I hardly noticed Peter in my first two years. But I got to know him quite well in my third year, thanks to one bond that we shared: We both needed to earn some money, and so we ended up working side by side in a chronic disease hospital.

Peter Keleman: Harvard Medical School 1952
Credit: Aesculapiad (Harvard Medical School Yearbook 1952)

My own background was limited in terms of both money and cultural opportunities. My grandfather was a farmer in the economically depressed hill country of eastern Kentucky. My father was a teacher who started out in a one-room schoolhouse and later became a school administrator. I grew up during the Depression. Poverty was prevalent in eastern Kentucky. I went to college and medical school on scholarships, but I needed money for room and board. Loans helped some, but I still needed to make money working part-time. As to cultural opportunities, they were few and far between in Appalachia.

Peter's background was quite different. He came from Budapest. His family had owned big clothing mills and highly successful businesses. Peter had had many cultural privileges in his childhood. By my standards, his family was incredibly rich. However, like many other rich Jewish families in Europe during the 1930s, they had to flee the country, leaving their wealth behind them. Now he needed to earn some money, just as I did. But he had been schooled in Budapest, Vienna, Oxford, and Harvard before entering medical school. I was in awe of his background and his cultural experiences.

So we ended up sharing a room, working part-time at the Holy Ghost Hospital for Incurable Diseases in Cambridge. And yes, that really was the name of this hospital owned by the Roman Catholic Archdiocese of Boston. The imposing, lantern-jawed Cardinal Richard Cushing presided over the archdiocese in those days. He had a loud, nasal voice that blared out the rosary over the hospital's loudspeakers at six each morning. It was quite a way for a non-Catholic such as myself to start each day. Nearly 60 years later, I can still recite the rosary. *Hail Mary, full of grace, blessed art thou among women ...*

This chronic disease hospital had many terminally ill patients. It was a pretty depressing place. One ward was filled with patients suffering from end-stage neurological diseases: multiple sclerosis, ALS (Lou Gehrig's disease), Parkinson's disease, and severe strokes with profound disabilities. Another ward was devoted to dying cancer patients. And so on. Our job, inexperienced as we were, was to take a medical history and do a complete physical examination on new admissions. We were also expected to respond to any medical emergencies and deal with any clinical problem that came up outside regular work hours. For our efforts we received room, board, laundry, and $25 a month. That covered most of my needs, since my tuition was taken care of through scholarships and loans.

The patients were technically the responsibility of a fully trained and licensed staff physician. However, in practice, this supervision usually amounted to a phone call giving us advice and verbal orders without coming in to see the patient. Bedside management, even for life-threatening problems, was often up to us—and the telephone and whomever we could get on the line for advice. At an incredibly early stage in our medical careers, we presided over deaths from a wide variety of diseases.

Even apart from the depressing condition of most of its patients, the hospital was an old, rather dreary, and unpleasant building. Nor was the atmosphere enhanced by the ubiquitous presence of black-robed nuns and crucifixes on the walls.

In this environment, and also under stress from the rigorous demands of medical school, those of us who worked at the Holy Ghost Hospital supported each other and became close friends. I particularly enjoyed getting to know Peter. He was like no one I had ever known. About five feet ten inches tall, lean, lithe, and graceful with curly brown hair and an appealing smile, he was a charming person. He was also left-handed, adding to his atypical image. His faint European accent added a hint of an intriguing background. Somehow it came as no surprise when we learned that he—and some unknown, but doubtless glamorous debutante—had recently won the annual waltz competition in Boston's stately Copley Plaza Hotel. It was an event high up on the social calendar of Boston. We assumed his dance partner was some beautiful young Beacon Hill socialite. We conjured up images of Peter and his partner whirling gracefully around the ballroom on a victory lap after their triumph. Try as we might to get all the details, though, Peter never told us much about that evening or his dance partner. He brushed away our questions, making the lady and the waltz contest both seem that much more exotic.

Peter was also a cellist. I assume that he was a good cellist, since he was good at everything else he did. But I never heard him play. He didn't keep his cello at the Holy Ghost Hospital, for security reasons. He would disappear from time to time, ostensibly to play his cello at the home of some relative. We wondered if he made side trips to beautiful socialites on Beacon Hill.

In summer Peter slipped away to Cape Cod, where he worked part-time as a tennis pro at a yacht club. I never saw him play tennis, but again I assume that he must have been quite good or he would not have been employed as a teaching pro. With his apparent proficiency in sports, music, and dance—and goodness knows what else—Peter symbolized to me the epitome of a cultured pre-war European gentleman, well- educated in all the social graces, as well as in the classroom.

He never studied much, and I doubt if he was anywhere near the top of our class. He seemed to have a busy life outside the classroom, including a part-time job. He knew that he could do respectably well without the effort expended by most of his classmates.

After graduation, I lost track of Peter. I was in over my head trying to meet the incredible demands of a surgical internship at the Peter Bent Brigham Hospital, a major Harvard teaching hospital, and I lost touch with most of my former classmates. For that matter, I more or less lost touch with my own life for that year.

In 1953, the last year of the Korean War, I was called up to active military duty in the "doctor draft." I was ordered to report to the Medical Field Officers' Service School at Fort Sam Houston, San Antonio, Texas. There the Army tried to teach young doctors the rudiments of military life.

Early in the Korean War, some Army units were

overrun by overwhelming numbers of North Korean and Chinese infantry. Many officers were killed or badly injured and unable to function. In some battalions, the battalion surgeon was the only surviving officer—and in command by virtue of military rank. Those doctors were totally unprepared to take over combat responsibilities. The results were disastrous. So the Army decreed that future battalion surgeons should go through a three-month crash course in military skills, including command responsibilities, if required.

By the end of three months, we had fired live weapons at targets simulating enemy soldiers. We had crawled under barbed wire while live tracer shells streaked red only a yard above our heads. From time to time, small explosive charges were detonated near us, simulating enemy artillery shells or land mines. We learned that you crawl under barbed wire on your back, leaving your hands free to cut or lift barbed wire or branches. The downside of crawling on your back was being face up. That position meant that dirt rained down on your face when explosive charges were detonated. And it was scary to see fiery red tracer shells streaking through the air only a yard above your head.

We walked in a horizontal line, carrying live ammunition in our rifles through "enemy" woods. From time to time, a dummy enemy soldier would pop up in the woods. We were expected to riddle his plywood body with bullets before he could do the same to us. During that simulated infantry advance, I kept a close watch to either side. I wanted to be sure that I did not get ahead of the scared and trigger-happy young doctors on either side of me—and therefore potentially in their line of fire.

I worried a lot more about the live ammunition in the rifles of those young doctors than I did about the pop-up dummies. We also learned how to use a compass and read a military map. But after three months, I still felt totally unprepared to take command of a battalion that had lost its regular army officers in actual combat.

Halfway through the course, I received my orders to the Far East. I was sent to Korea as a battalion surgeon and stationed just south of Seoul. Through the grapevine, I learned that Peter Kelemen had also been drafted and was already a battalion surgeon stationed just north of Seoul, near the DMZ, the demilitarized zone, a three-mile wide buffer that separated the U.S. Army from the North Korean and Chinese forces. Through some circuitous route that I no longer remember, I managed to contact Peter, and we arranged to meet and spend a day together in Seoul. I looked forward to seeing my old Holy Ghost Hospital roommate again. It was a bright spot in an otherwise drab and monotonous life after the armistice.

The much-awaited day finally arrived. I drove my jeep over 40 miles of rough dirt roads to Seoul. It took much longer than you might guess. The speed limit in the villages much of the way was five mph. It had been lowered to that frustratingly slow level ever since a $2,000 reparations payment had been paid to the family of a child killed when run over by an Army truck. It is hard to imagine now how much of a fortune $2,000 was to a Korean peasant in 1954. Other children from poor families were deliberately thrown under the wheels of military vehicles. So we were warned to watch out for the possible attempt to sacrifice a poor, unsuspecting child for the bounty. And so we were told to drive extremely slowly, especially when going through villages. With that concern added to the numerous potholes and other road hazards, I had a long slow drive to Seoul. Once there, I went to the designated meeting spot and waited for Peter. And waited ... and waited. But Peter never showed up.

Deeply disappointed, I drove back on the same potholed dirt road to our base. It seemed even slower and drearier going back than it had been driving up to Seoul. A month or so later, I learned that Peter had been killed by an enemy mine a few days before we had planned to meet in Seoul. The details of his death came to me later, through one of those coincidences so unlikely that I think maybe it was not a coincidence after all.

The following year, back in the United States, I was assigned to Fort Lewis, Washington. I was the commanding officer of the medical company of the 9th Infantry Regiment. The title was impressive, at least to me, but it was not a demanding assignment. My main job was to hold a daily sick call to evaluate and treat the illnesses and injuries of our regiment.

A young soldier who had served as a medical corpsman in Korea became a frequent patient in my sick call at Fort Lewis. He had a number of different complaints, starting with chronic fatigue, insomnia, headache, and anxiety attacks. He also had a terrifying recurrent nightmare that made him afraid to go to sleep and, whenever he was awakened by the nightmare, unable to get back to sleep. The nightmare actually was a vivid reliving of a military action he had seen in Korea. Today we would say that he had post-traumatic stress disorder. At that time, I had never heard of PTSD.

My patient had been a medical corpsman in a battalion aid station. One day the aid station received an emergency call. An infantry platoon had blundered into an enemy minefield. There were a number of casualties, unusual at the time, since a recent armistice was in effect. A three-mile-wide demilitarized buffer zone separated North Korean and Chinese soldiers from our troops. There were no more full-fledged battles, but there were occasional skirmishes of scouting parties. And there were many residual hazards of war, such as unexploded artillery shells or bombs and unidentified minefields. U.S. troops near the DMZ were emphatically warned not to walk in the countryside, where there were many old mines. But the poor Korean peasants, returning to their former villages by once familiar paths, sometimes set off a mine that killed or maimed them or their children.

Whenever a minefield was identified, usually by an unexpected accidental explosion of a mine, our orders were not to enter the area for any reason, not even to treat casualties, but simply to wait patiently until the engineers had cleared the minefield and verified that it was safe to enter. It was hard to stand on the sidelines when injured soldiers were screaming in pain and you had no idea how long it would be before the engineers arrived. But you also knew that entering the minefield might result in more casualties.

In his nightmare, my PTSD patient was reliving just such a scene. An infantry platoon had somehow blundered into a minefield. When the first mine exploded, killing and injuring several soldiers, others had panicked and tried to run back, retracing their steps. They exploded two more mines, causing still more casualties before the survivors just lay down on the ground, hoping that help would come soon from engineers and medics.

Word of the minefield casualties had been quick to get back to camp. The battalion surgeon, his first sergeant, and several corpsmen arrived by jeep in a few minutes. But the engineers were nowhere in sight. Nor did anyone know if they had been contacted. Nor where they were. Nor when they might be expected to arrive and clear the minefield, giving safe access to the wounded for the medics.

In the meantime, the casualties were pathetic. Their agonized cries for help were heart-rending. *Somebody help me! My God, please help! Where are the medics? I can't stand this pain. ... In the name of God, please help me!*

Finally, the battalion surgeon couldn't stand it any more. He had a bag of small syringes of morphine that would alleviate their pain. Maybe he could also stop some bleeding that might prove fatal if it went unchecked. He called out, *We are supposed to wait for the engineers, but we don't know when they will get here. While we wait, our buddies are suffering and may be dying. Who will volunteer to help me do what we can?*

My patient had cringed at the time. He was afraid to volunteer. He was only 20 years old and not very brave. He didn't speak up. Neither did anyone else. The risk was all too obvious. Finally, the first sergeant said, very quietly, "I'll go with you." And looking carefully at the ground for trip wires with each step they took, the battalion surgeon and his first sergeant started slowly toward the nearest casualties. Each step taken safely seemed like winning a small battle to the watching corpsmen.

Suddenly, the surgeon stumbled over the camouflaged trip wire to a "Bouncing Betty" mine, and a small charge of powder pushed the buried mine two or three feet into the air before the main charge exploded. The poor soul received the full force of the charge, rather than have some dissipated into the ground. The horrified corpsmen saw the mine jump up to the man's waist, explode with a blinding flash, and tear the man's body in half—his head, arms, and torso falling to one side; his pelvis and legs to the other. This scene was my patient's recurrent nightmare. The corpsman saw all the steps leading up to the explosion, knew exactly what was coming next, wanted desperately to call out and stop the inevitable from happening, only to see it happen again and again in his nightmares.

"What was the name of your battalion surgeon?" I asked. But in my heart, I knew already. I just hoped that I was wrong.

He replied softly, "Peter Kelemen."

Although I had expected it, I was still stunned by hearing Peter's name. And I was overwhelmed by the senseless tragedy of Peter's life ending like this. So suddenly. So violently. So irrevocably. What a waste of his enormous talent! How sad that his family fled Europe to give their son the promise of a better life, only to have his life end like this. How sad that Peter's brave and self-sacrificing desire to reduce the pain and suffering of others should have caused his own death. How unbelievably sad it all seemed! But apart from the sadness, I felt a sense of pride too, that Peter had knowingly put his own life at risk to help ease the suffering of his wounded comrades—however unwise it may have been.

I thought how sad that his sergeant had also died

following him, and how sad too that his medical corpsman, now my patient, suffered severe psychic scars from Peter's ill-advised—but ever so brave and well-meant—attempt to help the wounded soldiers from his battalion. What a terrible and senseless tragedy it all was! What a waste of human life, months after the war had supposedly been ended with the armistice.

I wondered how many other victims would be claimed by a war that had supposedly ended? How many Korean children would lose their legs or their lives to long-buried and long-forgotten land mines? My mind was a cauldron of such thoughts, a random crazy quilt of associations, all senseless and sad. I thought especially about the fact that my own life was just beginning, but Peter's life was suddenly over. At such an early age! Why him? Why not me? It could just as well have been me. I felt guilty. Life suddenly seemed unpredictable, capricious, and unfair. The game was a gamble. Why was I a winner—so far? Why had Peter lost—once and for all? Death seemed capricious, unpredictable, and senseless.

I could easily identify with Peter. It was painful to think he was dead. So, I adopted my first line of defense at dealing with death: I tried not to think about it.

CHAPTER 7

The Kamikaze Pilot's Widow

—

Peter's death made war and its aftermath seem senseless to me. That feeling was reinforced in a vivid way a few months after Peter's death. While still on assignment in Korea, I went to Japan on leave for rest and relaxation, R&R. It was a brief vacation from the Spartan life in the tents of Korea and an opportunity to get some good food for a change. In Korea we had no fresh fruits or vegetables, no milk or eggs (except in powdered form), no frozen foods or juices, and nothing very pleasing to the palate. However, good food was available in Japan.

Together in Tokyo with three other officers, I decided to search out a high-class restaurant and enjoy the first really good meal we had had in months. After a number of inquiries, we made a reservation at a restaurant reputed to be outstanding. After a hair-raising ride in a battered old taxi, we arrived at the restaurant and were immediately impressed by its tasteful facade and its colorful paper lanterns. The manager welcomed us with a low bow and asked us please to remove our shoes. Then he ushered us into a small private room, which was totally enclosed by bamboo: bamboo ceiling, bamboo floor, sliding bamboo panels forming the walls, and bamboo mats covering the floor. A long, low, black enamel table in the center of the room had silk cushions on both sides.

At the head of the table were a small hibachi and a larger silk cushion. A small, discreet floral arrangement graced the table, and yard-high palm shoots stood in pots at the corners of the room. Soft light came from paper lanterns hanging from the ceiling. The simple, pleasant space imparted a feeling of understated elegance. After we were seated on the cushions, the manager left, sliding the bamboo door closed behind him. We did not know what to expect next. The manager had little English, and we spoke no Japanese at all.

Before long, one of the bamboo wall panels slid noiselessly open. A beautiful, young Japanese woman stepped daintily into the room and quietly slid the panel closed again, leaving us totally private and alone in the room with her. She had jet-black hair swept up in a tight bun. She wore a long, peach-colored silk robe fastened with a maroon sash. Her eyes were as dark as her hair, and they were accentuated by her makeup. Her cheeks were powdered and pale white, dramatizing her bright red lipstick. We were enthralled by the vision. Was this a geisha girl, we wondered, and, by the way, exactly what is a geisha?

This beautiful young woman bowed low to each one of us. After this traditional formal Japanese greeting, she introduced herself. In a soft voice and with near-perfect English, she told us her name (which was Japanese and I no longer remember) and said that she would be our hostess for the evening. She put a jug of sake, a rather heavy and sweet rice wine, on the hibachi. When it was warm, she poured us each some sake in a small pottery cup. But she did not drink herself. She asked us each our name and where was our home. Were we married? If so, did we have children? If not, did we have a girl friend? Wasn't it hard to be separated? When were we going home? It was a comfortable, icebreaking conversation. And it seemed to establish a surprising degree of rapport between our exotic hostess and us. But it struck me that the talk was all about us.

While carrying on this facile cocktail conversation, our hostess was taking a bowl and some food items out of a drawer below the hibachi. She filled the bowl with various ingredients and put it over the coals. Before long, we had a bowl of delicious soup. And she gave us more sake with the soup.

The next course was more substantial and required some time to cook. While waiting, she asked if we would like to hear her sing. We said yes, of course. From behind a bamboo wall, she retrieved a small stringed instrument, somewhat like a guitar. She had a soft, pleasing voice and was quite proficient in playing the instrument. Between the singing, the conversation, and the food prepared at our table, time passed quickly. And we found ourselves feeling more and more warmly toward our charming hostess. Doubtless our warm feelings were enhanced by the increasing amounts of sake that we consumed.

After a while, we became curious about the background of our hostess. We asked her many of the same questions that she had asked us. Where did she live? What was her family like? Did she have a boy friend? A husband? How did she become a hostess in this restaurant? She was reluctant to open up her life to us at first, but she also wanted to remain friendly and gracious. And we believed, rightly I think, that she felt a genuine warmth and rapport toward us, just as we did toward her.

So, slowly, haltingly, a story emerged. She came from a small town, a distant suburb of Tokyo, where she grew up in a middle-class home with her parents and a younger brother. She did not have a boy friend, and she was not married. She had always liked music and had studied vocal and instrumental music in school, but she was not qualified to teach music and not able to make a living by performing. So she apprenticed to a restaurant owner to learn her present vocation, which she enjoyed. She liked being a hostess, and she met interesting people in her work.

We should have been satisfied with her story, but something seemed missing. Somehow the incongruity of the situation came to mind. It was 1954, less than a decade since the Japanese high command had surrendered to General Douglas MacArthur on the deck of the battleship Missouri. Only ten years ago, the Japanese had been our mortal enemies, guilty of a sneak attack on our Pacific fleet at Pearl Harbor and accused of many other atrocities while conquering much of the Pacific basin. These were the "dirty, yellow Japs" that I heard so much about while I was a teenager during World War II. But now the Japanese were our friends and allies. And presumably they now regarded us as friends and allies as well. Despite the fire bombing of Tokyo. Despite Hiroshima. Despite Nagasaki. Our tax dollars were being used to repair damage due to our own bombs. It boggled my mind. Our reviled enemies were now our good friends. And in such a short time!

"What was it like for you during the war?"

One of my companions suddenly pressed this question on our hostess with some urgency. I winced. I knew instinctively that I really didn't want to go where that question might lead us. The evening had been surprisingly pleasant, even memorable. Our hostess had been gracious, charming, and friendly. Why risk turning it all sour and leaving a bitter memory? And perhaps even more bitter in her memory?

Our hostess must have shared my reservations. Her face was devoid of expression, but she didn't reply for a minute. When she did, it was with some generalities. "It wasn't too bad. My town was never bombed. Food was scarce at times, though." I had the feeling that she was staying on safe ground. I also had the feeling that we were skirting the brink of a much deeper and more personal story, perhaps a more painful story. Her body language seemed to say as much. My companion, the one who pressed the question before, sensed the same reservations I was feeling.

"You are leaving something out. Please tell us what it was really like for you during the war."

He pleaded with her to tell us the whole story. She was slow to respond, not wanting to offend her guests, but also quite reluctant to share her life story with us.

"Please!"

Slowly, she looked up at each of us, then looked down at the floor for a minute and in a soft voice, she told us her story. As nearly as I can recall, this is what she said:

"Early in World War II, I was married to my high-school sweetheart. We were very young and very much in love. Our life together was not long. Soon my husband went off to war, along with all the other young men in our village. He was in the Navy, and he trained to be a pilot on an aircraft carrier. He liked to fly, and he told me that he was very good at it. He was in several naval battles and was awarded some medals.

"One day, a naval officer came to our house. He said that I should be quite proud. My husband had been given a great honor, one that was awarded only to the best and bravest pilots. He would be coming home to be honored by our mayor and our entire town. He would then go back to sea. He would not return. He had been selected as a kamikaze pilot. I was told that after a brief reunion, I would never see my husband again. Back at sea, when a major American warship, such as an aircraft carrier or a battleship, was identified, my husband would take off, intending to fly straight into its anti-aircraft fire and release his bombs at point-blank range. He would doubtless die in the attempt to destroy his victim. If by some miracle he survived, his gas tank had deliberately been filled only with enough gas to find his target, but not enough to make it back to his carrier. The Japanese navy took pains to ensure there would be no turning back and no second thoughts. My husband was as good as dead as soon as he was selected to be a kamikaze pilot. I wanted him to refuse, no matter what happened, but he felt his honor was at stake and there was no alternative.

"Our mayor arranged a great public ceremony in his honor. Several people spoke about his bravery and his patriotism. They said how proud our whole village was of my husband. It was like a funeral, but with the dead man able to enjoy the kind words said about him. After the ceremony was over, he was home for a few days. I couldn't enjoy the time. Even if he evaded the hero's death for which he had been selected, his shame would lead him to commit hari-kari later.

"After he went back to sea, I waited several weeks for the knock on my door. When it came, I was composed and ready. The naval officer who came to the door was quite elated. He said that I should be very proud. On his fatal last flight, my husband was credited with sinking an American aircraft carrier in the Battle of Midway."

I felt a sudden chill. I knew about that aircraft carrier. It was the USS Yorktown, hero of the Battle of the Coral Sea. However, at the Battle of Midway, a Japanese dive-bomber had flown directly through its anti-aircraft fire and delivered a full payload of bombs into its command center. Totally disabled and unable to move, the carrier was an easy target for a torpedo from a nearby Japanese submarine. The USS Yorktown was a huge ship with a large crew. And most of the crew drowned.

I felt more and more uneasy. My stomach became unsettled. I almost felt like throwing up. Before her story unfolded, I had had a pleasant, slightly drowsy feeling that I attributed to the sake. Now, I was suddenly wide-awake and distinctly ill at ease, both physically and psychologically. I knew about the USS Yorktown. I knew about its sinking in the Battle of Midway. I knew about the great loss of life. Its sinking was a great national tragedy at the time. And now I was being served a pleasant meal and entertained graciously by the widow of the Japanese pilot who sank that carrier and killed all those sailors.

This is crazy, I thought. War makes no sense. This young woman is a victim of the war. She lost her husband. But her husband killed hundreds of guys like me. They were his victims. And now, a few years later, his beautiful widow is my gracious hostess. I am her grateful customer. We have established a brief, but meaningful friendship. We like each other. Why did our countries have to fight each other? What did all those deaths accomplish? It makes no sense.

The magic had gone out of the evening. Hearing her story, we became quiet and somber. We thanked her for sharing her story. We expressed our sadness on hearing about the death of her husband. We thanked her for the food she had prepared, for the songs she had sung and, especially, for making us feel welcome and comfortable far from our native land. She bowed low, thanked us for coming, and gracefully ushered us out.

That dinner was nearly 60 years ago, but I remember it vividly. I will always remember it. It reminded me so forcefully of how many lives have been lost in wars. And how we assuage our grief, and perhaps our guilt, by making heroes of the dead. Some wars are perhaps just and necessary, but all too many have done little good and have killed and maimed many innocent people.

The Professional Years: Many Faces of Death

CHAPTER 8

A Life in My Hands

—

When I decided to become a surgeon, I knew the responsibility could be heavy. My training in cardiac surgery brought that fact home to me in a forceful way. Cardiac surgery was then a new field. Procedures and equipment were just being developed. The learning curve was steep. And the price for advances in the field was often the life of an early patient … and the peace of mind of the surgeon. It was a heavy price on both sides. I was never comfortable with the high stakes involved.

"Do you want to put your finger in the heart?"

I was asked that question in a cardiac operating room in 1957. I was the senior resident on the cardio-thoracic service of the Peter Bent Brigham Hospital in Boston. To be more specific, I was first assistant on an operation to open a constricted heart valve. It was called mitral valvuloplasty. Dr. Dwight Harken, the surgeon, had developed that procedure. He was one of the pioneers of early cardiac surgery. Trained originally as a thoracic surgeon and specializing in tuberculosis, cancer, and infectious diseases of the lung, Dr. Harken gained fame in World War II for successfully repairing battle wounds of the heart, sometimes removing shrapnel while the heart was beating. There were no heart-lung machines then. After the war, he used his battlefield experience to repair heart valves damaged by rheumatic fever.

Dwight Harken, MD, Chief of Peter Brent Brigham Hospital Cardio-thoracic Surgery: a pioneer cardiac surgeon who often had to deal with death
Credit: Aesculapaid (Harvard Medical School Yearbook 1952)

Rheumatic heart disease, caused by streptococcal infections, was common then. Before antibiotics became available, streptococcal infections were hard to treat. They caused inflammation of heart valves, often followed by scar tissue and calcification that impaired valve function. Especially vulnerable was the mitral valve, which controls blood flow into the main pumping chamber of the heart. Dr. Harken had learned how to insert his index finger into the heart and break open the calcified scar tissue, opening the mitral valve and allowing more blood to flow through it. The procedure was life saving. Patients came from all over the world to Boston in order to have Dr. Harken operate on them. He was a flamboyant and striking figure: about five feet ten inches tall, with a sturdy frame, large eyeglasses, and a shock of red hair.

Somewhat impatiently, Dr. Harken said once again, "Do you want to put your finger in the heart or not?" He was not someone to keep waiting for an answer. I knew his offer was a compliment and he expected me to be thrilled.

So I said, "Yes, I certainly would." But I was scared.

I had assisted Dr. Harken on several of these mitral valve procedures, and I knew his routine. The key to the operation was a small saclike appendage on the left auricle, which is the heart chamber that collects oxygen-rich blood from the lungs and returns it to be pumped out to the body. The mitral valve allows blood to flow out from the left auricle into the left ventricle, and it prevents blood from flowing back when the ventricle contracts. When a surgeon inserts a finger through the auricular appendage into the left auricle, he can feel the constricted mitral valve and enlarge its opening. The trick is to create a hole in the heart to work through without causing bleeding.

Dr. Harken had an ingenious solution to the problem. He sewed a strong silk suture around the base of the auricular appendage in purse-string fashion. Then he placed a surgical clamp across the base, just tight enough to prevent bleeding. Next, he cut off the top of the appendage and inserted his index finger. The clamp was opened just enough to allow insertion of the finger, and the purse-string suture was snugged up around the finger to prevent any bleeding. Now the surgeon could feel the valve and stretch it open.

I followed this routine easily until I had my finger in the heart. Things were going well! It was exciting but scary. I could feel the heart beating around my finger.

"See if you can crack the valve open."

I had not expected that command. Timidly, I felt the valve. It was hard and calcified. I tried to stretch it open, but it was too stiff.

"Push harder! You are too gentle!"

I tried again, with more force. Nothing happened. I was afraid of using more force than I could control and causing a major complication. I could break off a calcified fragment of the valve that would be swept up into the brain, causing a stroke. Or I could break open the valve in the wrong place, making it incompetent and allowing blood to flow back from the ventricle, as well as forward, limiting cardiac output. Or I could tear the thin wall of the auricle, causing bleeding that would be hard to control. There were many ways for an inexperienced young surgeon to do harm with a finger in a diseased heart!

Reluctantly, I said, "I would like for you to take over."

Dr. Harken replaced me. He used more force and fractured the calcified valve wide open, with immediate improvement in cardiac output. There were no complications. I was glad that he had succeeded—and that I had not done any harm.

Early cardiac surgery had a high mortality at the Brigham. There had been seven previous attempts to correct mitral valve disease in the late 1920s. The surgeon was Dr. Elliott Cutler, a distinguished surgeon and the surgeon in chief at the Brigham. All seven patients died, and the procedure was abandoned—until Dr. Harken arrived two decades later.

By the time that I was assigned to the cardiothoracic service, mitral valve repair had become standardized and had a low mortality. But aortic valve replacement was just getting underway. It involved using a new heart-lung machine and replacing the diseased valve with a metal and plastic artificial valve. I was told that seven of the first 12 patients died. These early patients were near death from their disease, and the operation was a desperate attempt to save them. I felt sorry for the patients who died and their families, but also for the surgeon. I know how emotionally wrenching it is to lose a patient you have operated on.

I used to think that some cardiac surgeons were just naturally detached from their patient's outcome. They seemed to remain calm, cool, and collected no matter what happened. A prime example of this remarkable self-control was Dr. Robert Gross, chief of surgery at the Children's Hospital in Boston. He was an early pioneer of pediatric cardiac surgery, developing new procedures for congenital cardiac anomalies. There was an understandably high mortality in these new procedures carried out on small, desperately ill children. But Dr. Gross's straight black hair was never out of place, and his impassive face never betrayed any emotion. My fellow residents felt that ice water circulated in his veins, until one day something happened that betrayed his true feelings. A close friend of mine who worked with Dr. Gross told me this story:

It had been a rough week. Several children had died during or shortly after surgery. Their parents had been inconsolable. After the last death, Dr. Gross went straight from the operating room to his office. He told his secretary to cancel all scheduled procedures and wait for further instructions. He said nothing more: no explanation, no contact information, and no designation of another surgeon to take over in his absence. It was bizarre. No one knew where Dr. Gross was going or when he would return. It was the talk of the hospital.

Four or five days later, Dr. Gross finally called his

office. He was in Bermuda! He had driven from his office directly to Boston's Logan Airport. He had scanned the list of flights and gotten a ticket on one about to leave for Bermuda. He desperately needed to get away! He was in no state of mind to do another life-or-death operation on a sick child. To do his best for the child, he needed to rest and relax. When he felt back to normal, he called Boston and rescheduled his pending operations. The patients did well.

The friend who told me this story said that Dr. Gross was really a warm and sensitive person. He just kept his feelings under tight control. He believed that maintaining a stoic image by the surgeon was best for all concerned. Above all else, having a calm, cool surgeon in a crisis was best for the patient. But underneath that calm exterior, carefully hidden from view, powerful emotions were sometimes raging. Sometimes even the calmest of surgeons may need to fly to Bermuda.

After finishing my training with Dr. Harken, I thought about becoming a cardiac surgeon. It was a new field, full of exciting challenges. I finished my surgical training at West Roxbury Veterans Affairs Hospital, where Dr. Richard Warren was just starting a cardiac surgery program.

Dr. Warren asked me to assist him in some of his early cardiac procedures. It seemed like a good chance for me to find out if I wanted to take on the challenges of a career in the new field of cardiac surgery.

Chief of surgery and a bona fide Boston blueblood, Dr. Warren was the seventh member of his family to become a Harvard professor of surgery. His lineage dated back to John Warren, one of three founders of Harvard

Medical School. John Warren's older brother, Joseph, was also a surgeon but better known as a Revolutionary War hero, a major general who was killed in the Battle of Bunker Hill on June 17, 1775. It was Dr. Joseph Warren who ordered Paul Revere's famous ride.

In 1846 John Warren's son, John Collins Warren, was the first surgeon to do an operation under ether anesthesia, making new surgical procedures possible and greatly relieving the pain of surgery. John Collins Warren was also the first dean of Harvard Medical School, which had been founded by his father. Richard Warren upheld the family medical heritage.

Richard Warren, MD: He resigned his position as Chief of Surgery at the West Roxbury VA Hospital, creating a vacancy for me.

I had been in awe of him since medical school, when he had been my instructor in surgery. About 50 years old then, he was nearly six feet tall and had a trim athletic build. His slightly curly brown hair was just starting to show some streaks of gray. He had the square jaw and the classic features of a movie star. His bedside manner was reassuring, helpful, and caring. He was a great role model for medical students.

Dr. Warren was a broadly trained general surgeon

and one of the founders of vascular surgery. He developed ways to improve the blood flow to the leg and prevent amputation. When amputation was unavoidable, he was a strong advocate of saving as much tissue as possible in order to improve later function.

It was natural that Dr. Warren should use techniques developed to restore blood flow in the legs to restore blood flow in the heart as well. It was not easy. The arteries of the heart are smaller than those of the leg. Techniques used to remove blockages in leg arteries did not work so well in the arteries of the heart. To work on coronary arteries required stopping the heart and using a heart-lung machine, still being refined in those days. Worst of all, the small arteries of the heart were more apt to clot off than larger leg arteries. Often, they clotted off while the patient was still in the operating room. It was discouraging. Before new techniques were standardized by trial and error, the operative mortality was high.

My job in these early procedures with Dr. Warren was to open and close the chest and to position the heart in the best way for the surgeon to work on the blocked coronary arteries. I also set up the heart-lung machine, so the heart could be stopped without stopping blood flow to the rest of the body. I did the busy-work. Dr. Warren or one of his senior associates tried to open the coronary arteries, tease out the plaque blocking them, and sew the arteries closed again. The ideal way to do this had yet to be worked out. The surgeon was in uncharted waters. Often, plans did not work out. Even if the blockage could be removed, the artery might be blocked again by a fresh blood clot. Sometimes the patient died on the operating room table. The pressure on the surgeon was enormous.

Dr. Warren was often in need of a trip to Bermuda, but he did not take one.

Helping on those unsuccessful operations to restore blood flow through blocked coronary arteries was hard on me too. Although the surgeon was in charge, the first assistant was an important part of the team and shared responsibility for the outcome. I was often the one asked to break the bad news to the family waiting anxiously in the lounge. I hated the long walk down the corridor on my way to dash their hopes.

The death of one patient is indelibly seared in my memory. His operation had not gone well. It had been difficult to core out the obstructing plaque. The lining of the artery was left ragged and raw, inviting the formation of a clot later. The heart-lung machine had been disconnected, and conductive paddles placed front and back on the heart. An electric shock had been administered. The heart resumed its beat. But the beat was feeble. The heart muscle, starved by lack of blood flow for too long, urgently needed some help to strengthen its beat. Now, cardiac surgeons have various devices to assist a failing heart, but then they had nothing but their own hands to do open cardiac massage.

I had never done open cardiac massage, but I knew how to do it: Place the right hand behind the heart, and the left hand over the front. Forcefully squeeze the heart, from the apex to the base, ejecting blood out into the body. It is important to squeeze hard, but with the palms, not the fingers. The tip of a finger can go right through the thin wall of the right ventricle—a disastrous complication.

Open cardiac massage is tiring. After a minute or

two, a fresh pair of hands is needed. The operating team members take turns spelling each other. Fortunately, today it is rarely necessary with modern techniques and equipment available.

The senior surgeon on this operation started open cardiac massage, but soon passed off the job to me. I alternated with another resident for a few more minutes. The heart was not beating at all now. The surgeon pronounced the patient dead, but he said the rest of the team could continue to massage the heart if we would feel better. And he left. I was now in charge. I wanted the man to have every chance to live, even if that chance was only one in 1,000. So we continued.

In a few minutes, the anesthesiologist stood up from his stool at the head of the operating table. He signaled to me to lean over the surgical drapes that blocked my view of the patient. When I did, I could see the patient's face.

His eyes were open!

He was gazing around with a dreamy, detached look. There was no hint of pain or fear. I was startled by his appearance. It made no sense. He was anesthetized. His heart was not beating. He had even been pronounced dead. But he was obviously still conscious—because of my hands squeezing his heart. His life was literally in my hands! And my hands were tired and aching. How long could I last?

Without thinking, I leaned over the drapes and said, "Close your eyes and go back to sleep. Everything is OK."

It was a lie. I winced, even as I said it. Everything was not OK. He was about to die. And I was desperately trying to comfort him. Slowly, his eyelids fluttered shut. His situation was hopeless. We continued to massage his heart a few more minutes and then gave up. His eyes never opened again. I felt terrible. The anesthesiologist told me that he had stopped giving anesthetic drugs to avoid any toxicity to a failing heart. The patient woke up as a result, but seemed not to be suffering any pain. It was remarkable! And it was quite unsettling to me.

I decided not to become a cardiac surgeon. There were bound to be many deaths until the field matured. And the many deaths would weigh heavily on my shoulders. I felt that if I became a cardiac surgeon, I should do nothing else but strive to reduce the mortality. I should minimize any time spent on teaching, research, or administrative duties. The price was too high.

CHAPTER 9

Premonitions

—

One day in the early 1960s, my morning mail contained a handwritten envelope, addressed to me at the VA hospital. The return address was Fitchburg, an industrial town about 40 miles away. I didn't recognize the address, and I opened the envelope with curiosity. A black-and-white photograph fell out of the envelope onto my desk. One glance, and a chill ran down my spine. I knew that man only too well. He was a recent patient of mine. Let's call him Bill. A healthy 40-year-old truck driver, Bill had been admitted to the hospital with an asymptomatic groin hernia. Now, in the picture, he lay still and pale in his coffin, his eyes closed as if sleeping. An American flag was draped over the lower half of the casket.

There was an accompanying letter from Bill's live-in girl friend. Let's call her Diane. She wrote to say how much she appreciated all my efforts to save Bill's life. And she wanted me to know what a nice funeral the VA had provided Bill, all paid for at government expense. The gruesome picture of Bill lying peacefully in his casket was her way of showing me. Her letter of gratitude didn't make me feel any better about Bill's death, although that was clearly her intention. Instead, once again, I felt drenched through-and-through with guilt and shame. Healthy 40-year-old men shouldn't die after a routine hernia repair! Somehow we should have prevented it! But Diane said that I shouldn't feel responsible, that the outcome was fated from the start, that her boy friend had even sensed his impending death before being admitted to the hospital. I only wish that she had told me that story before the operation.

Bill's medical history was simple. He had applied and was accepted for a good-paying job with a large trucking firm, subject to passing a routine medical examination. But the exam showed a previously unsuspected groin hernia. The company said that since the job required heavy lifting, the hernia would have to be repaired before they could give him a job. And since he was a veteran, he chose to go to a VA facility where his care would be free.

His medical work-up was unremarkable. His chest X-ray, electrocardiogram, and routine blood and urine examinations were all normal. He was scheduled for surgery the morning after hospital admission.

We usually did groin hernia operations under spinal anesthesia or by injecting the nerves to the groin region with a short-duration anesthetic. However, some patients preferred general anesthesia. They wanted to be "put to sleep." They often said that they "didn't want to know what's going on" or that they were "afraid of needles," especially in the spine. Bill wanted to be put to sleep. In retrospect, it was a tragic choice. The general anesthesia seemed to be routine, including use of an endotracheal tube to safeguard the airway while the patient was unconscious. The surgery also seemed to be routine. After a brief stay in the recovery room until the anesthesia had worn off, Bill was sent back to his hospital room, which he shared with three other men. His initial recovery from surgery was uneventful: some mild incisional pain, as expected, and a low-grade temperature, not uncommon after surgery. The next day, though, things began to change. Bill said that he didn't feel well. He didn't look well either. He had developed a cough, and his temperature was elevated. We ordered some lab work, including a chest X-ray. The white blood cell count was elevated and the chest X-ray showed some white streaks in both lungs, indicating increased bronchial secretions. We ordered a sputum culture and a pulmonary disease consultation.

A worried young woman named Diane sat by Bill's bedside all that day. We assumed she was Bill's wife. She was quite concerned about his condition. It was obvious that she loved him. We tried to keep her closely informed about all that we knew and all that we planned to do. She was hungry for any information about Bill and was always grateful when we took the time to talk to her.

The pulmonary disease consultant came up with an unexpected conclusion. He thought that Bill had a case of what was commonly referred to as the Hong Kong flu, a particularly virulent type of influenza that was sweeping the world at that time, bringing back memories of the influenza pandemic of 1918–1919, in which 20 million people died worldwide. The Hong Kong flu had started in Asia and spread rapidly to America. There had been a few deaths reported, mainly in the elderly or chronically ill, but I wasn't aware of any deaths in healthy young adults like Bill. So I was reassured by the consultant's diagnosis.

But Bill didn't get better. Instead, he got steadily worse. He developed a productive cough and a high temperature. His breathing became labored. His chest X-ray showed snowy patches in both lungs, suggesting pneumonia. The phlegm he coughed up contained green and yellow streaks of pus. By now, I was quite alarmed. We switched antibiotics from the routine penicillin/streptomycin combination then in vogue, to the newer, and much more expensive, so-called broad-spectrum antibiotics. We hoped the more powerful antibiotics would kill the bacteria making Bill so sick, just as penicillin had once wiped out the deadly pneumonia due to the pneumococcus in a seemingly miraculous way.

But that didn't happen to Bill. Instead, the infection in his lungs marched inexorably onward. The blood oxygen level became worrisomely low, and it failed to improve, even when 100 percent oxygen was delivered by a facemask. Reluctantly, we decided to put Bill on a ventilator. I hated to do so. It required us to intubate him. He could no longer talk to us or to Diane. Still, being intubated would allow us to suction out the thick pus that Bill no longer had the strength to cough up. Reducing those infected secretions might help. The ventilator could do the work of breathing. Maybe that could help too. We were desperate to do something—anything—that might help.

A simple surgical procedure had turned into a surgeon's worst nightmare. And the patient's worst nightmare too. How could someone be fighting for his life after such a routine operation? I was reminded of an old surgical axiom: There is no such thing as a "minor" operation. (And, most especially, if the operation is on you.)

The ventilator helped a bit. The blood oxygen level

improved, and we were able to suction out some thick yellow-green secretions. We tried to encourage Bill, who was quite passive. He looked bewildered. Diane sat by his bedside, holding his hand, saying very little. Bill was unable to speak, of course, because of the tube in his throat. He lay quietly in bed with his eyes closed, as if asleep and waiting for this bad dream to run its course. And run its course it did ... relentlessly downhill.

After brief improvement on the respirator, Bill's condition worsened steadily. His temperature stayed in the range of 103 to 104 F, his pulse rate speeded up, and his blood pressure began to fall. None of the antibiotics and other medications that we gave in desperation seemed to help. Consultants from the other Harvardteaching hospitals had nothing new to offer. The consensus was that Bill had a depressed immune system as a result of the Hong Kong flu and that his body was unable to combat a highly aggressive, antibiotic-resistant bacterial pneumonia. So, we watched and waited and did what we could. Unfortunately, it was not enough. Bill's blood pressure fell to shock levels and his heart finally stopped beating.

We were distraught. We could hardly believe that Bill was dead, that a healthy man had not survived a routine hernia operation. We were frustrated that we could not save his life. We felt guilty, but we didn't know what we could have done differently. Naturally, we wanted to have an autopsy to tell us as much as possible about why Bill had been unable to combat his infection and why we had been unable to help. We asked Diane for permission to do an autopsy.

And then we found out, for the first time, that

Diane was not his wife. His legal wife had never visited him. The woman who was constantly with him throughout his hospital course was a live-in girl friend, namely Diane. It was a complicated story.

According to Diane, Bill had asked his wife for a divorce for several years. She had steadfastly refused. Bill had finally moved out and lived alone until he met Diane. They fell in love and decided to live together, even if Bill's wife still would not agree to a divorce.

Diane tearfully recalled driving up with Bill into the hospital grounds. He turned into the parking lot and parked the car, but he did not get out of the car.

"Is something wrong, Honey?" Diane realized that Bill was quite troubled. There was no response. His face was pale. And anxious.

"What's wrong, Bill?"

"I just have the strangest feeling that if I go into that hospital, I'm never coming out alive."

Diane was shocked. After a moment, she said, "Let's go home."

Bill didn't respond for a while. Finally, he said, "I guess I've just got a bad case of cold feet."

Neither said anything for a while.

"Let's go home anyway."

He shook his head. "Honey, we need this job. We need the money. I'm just having an attack of nerves. It will pass. I'll be OK." But he didn't sound convinced.

So they talked in the parking lot for a long time. About the job. About the VA hospital's good reputation, about their future life together. And about their money problems. She felt they should go home. He felt they needed the job and one day would look back on his "case of cold feet" and smile. Finally, he got out of the car and walked into the admitting office. Reluctantly, she followed.

Getting back to Bill's story: We finally tracked down the legal wife. She never came into the hospital, but she was willing to give verbal permission for an autopsy over the phone. She didn't seem to care what had happened to Bill. She wasn't even curious to know the results of the autopsy.

In fact, the autopsy didn't come up with any new information. Both lungs were pretty much destroyed by a bacterial pneumonia. That overwhelming infection had also damaged other vital organs, especially the kidneys. The hernia repair was entirely normal. The autopsy findings were consistent with depleted immune function from the Hong Kong flu, setting the stage for a fulminating pneumonia due to bacteria that were resistant to all the antibiotics we had available. I felt that we finally understood what had happened, but I still felt terrible about Bill's death. I wondered if the medical history and physical examination done on hospital admission failed to detect early flu-like symptoms that would have led to canceling the surgery. Or if Bill became aware of such early symptoms but attributed them to his "cold feet." I will never know—and I will always feel bad about Bill's death.

Although we were finally able to understand the medical reasons for Bill's unexpected death, I have never been able to explain his premonition. It seems to hint at a glimpse of the future on Bill's part. But how is that possible? And Bill is only one of several patients of mine who had a premonition that later turned out to be true.

For my part, after Bill's death, I never carried out an elective operation when I heard that the patient had a strong premonition that it would turn out badly. I am not talking about the uneasy qualms that many of us feel before major surgery or a plane trip or a wedding or many other major life events. I am talking about a gut-wrenching conviction that the outcome will be bad.

Call me superstitious. Call me gullible. Call me naive. Still, I take premonitions seriously, even if I can't explain how they happen. I have heard too many premonitions that proved to be true. And others have been described to me by people whom I trust completely. For example, early in my surgical training, one of my teachers was Dr. Francis Newton. He was a distinguished older surgeon with thin, silvery hair and steel-rimmed glasses. He was quiet and soft-spoken, but he tolerated no nonsense. I regarded Dr. Newton as a master surgeon with many years of experience. He was formerly the chief of general surgery at the Brigham, but now semi-retired. All the residents looked up to him. One day in the fall of 1952, when I was just starting my surgical internship, Dr. Newton sat down with me to have lunch in the hospital cafeteria. Other residents joined us. It was a privilege for us to talk to Dr. Newton.

One of the residents was excited about his plans to fly to a national surgical meeting. Dr. Newton made the casual comment that he had never taken a plane flight. We could hardly believe it. Why not? We pressed him for an explanation. Dr. Newton then said that as a young man he had promised someone that he would never take a plane flight unless it was absolutely necessary. And in his entire career, it had never been absolutely necessary.

But there was more to the story than that.

*Francis Newton, MD: a respected Peter Bent Brigham Hospital surgeon
whose life was saved by his landlady's vivid dream
Credit: Aesculapiad (Harvard Medical School Yearbook 1949)*

In the early 1920s, Dr. Newton was a young surgeon in training and had spent a year studying in London. He stayed in a rooming house and became friendly with his landlady, a grandmotherly woman who became quite fond of him. Toward the end of his time in London, he decided to spend a week in Paris, flying across the English Channel. He had never flown before and was looking forward eagerly to his first flight. Airline travel was new and exciting then. However, the day before he was to leave, his landlady came to his room, agitated and distraught. She begged him not to fly to Paris. He told her how much he looked forward to the trip. She started crying and said that if he took the plane, she knew that he would surely die.

The night before, she had had a vivid nightmare. In her dream, she saw Dr. Newton's plane struggle to maintain altitude and then plunge into the sea. She knew at once that there were no survivors. She woke in a panic. She knew that it was only a dream. But it was so real, so vivid. It didn't feel like any ordinary dream. It felt more like a prophecy. The more she thought about it, the more convinced she became that she had been given a look into the future to warn her American renter what was about to happen to him. Dr. Newton tried to reassure her, but she would not be reassured. Tearfully, she begged and begged him not to fly. Finally, he reluctantly agreed to change his plans.

The next day, the plane Dr. Newton was to have taken crashed in the English Channel. There were no survivors. The cause was never determined.

Shaken by his narrow escape, Dr. Newton promised his landlady—and himself—that he would never fly anywhere unless it was absolutely necessary. And over the next 30 years, flying had never been absolutely necessary.

A premonition had saved Dr. Newton's life. He could never explain his landlady's glimpse into the future. It seemed impossible to a surgeon trained in a scientific worldview. Still, he felt enormously fortunate that he had changed his plans.

Like Dr. Newton, I cannot explain premonitions, but I no longer ignore them. Maybe some day science will catch up and provide an explanation for what now seems to be a mystery.

CHAPTER 10

Little Bubbles That Kill

—

One Sunday morning, just as I was finishing morning rounds, I was paged by one of the medical residents. He asked me to come to the medical floor and take a quick look at a patient they had just admitted. The patient appeared to have a simple thigh infection, but seemed sicker and had a much higher temperature than expected with most superficial infections. The resident wondered if there might be an abscess that needed to be drained surgically. He didn't sound particularly worried, and I didn't get any sense of urgency about the requested consult. So it was nearly lunchtime before I went down to see the patient.

The patient was about 50 years old but looked older. He was unshaven, and his gray hair was tousled. His face had lines that reflected a hard life. It was a battle-weary face. I was not surprised to find out that he was a heavy smoker and a heavy drinker as well. He had no family and no fixed address. He was one of those World War II vets who had left the service with severe psychosocial problems that left him without the resources needed to cope with life. For such down-and-out veterans, VA hospitals often became a safe port in the ever-raging storm of their daily lives. There they could count on a warm room, a bed, three hot meals a day, a canteen and recreation hall, and usually a cadre of like-minded souls with whom to socialize.

Some of those poor veterans actively searched for ways to be admitted to a VA hospital. Some learned to fake common illnesses. Some were truly ill, often from some chronic disease that they deliberately didn't treat as they had been advised. They actually welcomed complications that would qualify them for hospital admission. In winter they often found their way south to VA hospitals in warmer climates. The VA hospital at Coral Beach, Florida, was a favorite goal, for example. When the weather turned hot, they found their way back to the North, and once again turned up in our ER. We called these patients "snowbirds."

Alcoholism was a common problem in these patients, as were peptic ulcer disease and emphysema and other conditions brought on and aggravated by heavy smoking. If neglected, almost any of these serious chronic diseases could justify hospital admission.

The patient I was asked to see had a diagnosis of "diabetes with cellulitis" listed as the cause of his admission. The resident had taken a medical history, which was notable mainly for the fact that the previous day the patient had injected himself with insulin in the front of his right thigh, at just the spot where he now had pain and redness of the skin. The medical resident suspected that the patient had used poor sterile technique and inadvertently injected germs along with the insulin, leading to a local infection. The medical conundrum was that the patient now had a temperature of 103 degrees, complained bitterly of pain at the injection site, and looked much sicker than would be expected with a simple skin infection.

The physical examination wasn't very dramatic. The slightly reddened area of skin was six or eight centimeters in diameter. I touched it gently to look for any suggestion of an abscess. At one place I felt a peculiar bubbly sensation: suggestive evidence of air or some other gas in the tissues being examined. I could actually feel little bubbles of gas rolling around in the tissue under my fingers. It was an unusual finding.

Why would there be air or any other gas in that location? I vaguely recalled reading about "gas gangrene," a not uncommon condition in the trench warfare of World War I. It occurred in war wounds contaminated by the dirt of fields or barnyards. Farm animals frequently harbor a family of particularly virulent bacteria in their gut. The scientific name is Clostridia. These organisms are among the most lethal known to medical science. Ordinary antibiotics do not touch them. In World War I, clostridial infections were almost uniformly fatal, except in patients where only the foot or lower leg was involved. These patients often survived after a mid-thigh amputation through clean, uninfected tissue. Removing the lower infected area and leaving the wound open was about the only treatment that worked.

Clostridial organisms can be identified under the microscope fairly easily when stained with certain dyes. The large, rod-shaped bacilli have a thick capsule that turns blue on routine staining. So I suggested to the medical resident that he fill a syringe with sterile saline solution and inject it into the area where I could feel gas bubbles. Then he should massage the area gently for a few seconds and suck back as much fluid as possible to examine under the microscope after appropriate staining. This might take an hour or two, I thought, so I went home for Sunday dinner with my family, leaving instructions to call me at home when the results were available.

I was just finishing dinner when the medical resident called. Under the microscope he had seen many large, rod-shaped organisms with dark blue capsules, proof of a clostridial infection. We had a patient with the much-feared "gas gangrene" of World War I. I called the surgical resident to notify the OR and the anesthesia department to set up for an emergency operation to remove all infected tissue.

I no longer remember what I said to the patient. He seemed dazed, almost comatose, and looked much more toxic than before. His temperature was now 104 degrees. Equally striking was the growth in the size of the area on his thigh where I could feel bubbles of gas. I knew that we had no time to waste. We went straight to the OR.

The anesthesiologist had started two intravenous lines, put on a blood pressure cuff, and inserted a urinary catheter to monitor urine output. He had also administered some pre-op medications and prepared to insert a breathing tube. In the meantime, the surgical resident and I scrubbed the abdomen and both thighs, painted them with a germ-killing solution, and draped off the operative area with sterile towels. To my surprise, the area where we could feel little bubbles now seemed larger than I remembered from my exam just a few minutes before. I took a skin-marking pencil and drew a line around the tissue I planned to remove. It was a fairly long distance away from the area where I could feel gas bubbles under the skin. I knew that it was important to remove every bit of infected tissue and that no antibiotics would destroy any killer germs left behind. I hoped that the infection would only involve the skin and the underlying fat, but I was prepared to remove any deeper tissues that were infected as well.

By this time, the anesthesiologist was hidden from our view by the sterile drapes. He was seated on a stool at the patient's head. Usually, the anesthesiologist gives the go-ahead to the surgeon when the patient is fully anesthetized and ready for surgery.

In this case, several minutes went by and there was only silence from the head of the table. I could not see what the anesthesiologist was doing. After a brief while, I asked impatiently, "Can I go ahead?"

"Not yet," he replied, sounding preoccupied with whatever he was doing.

After a few moments, I said, "Is there a problem?"

"Yes," he said. "Whenever I give him even a little bit of pentothal [a routine short-acting barbiturate used for many operations in those days], the bottom drops out of his blood pressure. I'm afraid to give him enough anesthesia to permit surgery. He might go into irreversible shock. So I'm trying to increase his blood volume with intravenous fluids. I hope the situation will improve."

It seemed there was nothing for me to do but wait for the anesthesiologist to improve the patient's condition, so I turned my attention back to the proposed surgery. It seemed to me that the gas bubbles had spread right up to the lines marking my proposed incision, even in the few minutes we had been getting ready. I needed a wide margin of normal tissue to be sure that I had removed every bit of infected tissue. So I took the skin marking pencil again and made a much bigger line enclosing a larger excision.

In the meantime, the anesthesiologist had been unable to raise the blood pressure with intravenous fluids and had sent to the blood bank for transfusions. My surgical team, already scrubbed, gowned, gloved, and ready for surgery, just stood by the operating table, arms folded, frustrated and surprised by the delay. We did not understand the dramatic battle going on in the patient's body. Gas gangrene bacilli were pouring out powerful toxins, as were the dying cells that the germs had attacked. The toxins were poisoning the heart, kidneys, and other vital organs. None of us in that operating room had ever encountered anything quite like this situation before.

The gas bubbles in the patient's thigh were spreading outward, even as we waited. I drew an even bigger circle of intended excision, extending now up into the groin and lower abdomen.

"Shouldn't we just go ahead?" I asked the anesthesiologist, feeling frustrated.

"Have you noticed the patient's urine?" he replied.

I stepped back to look at the plastic bag into which the urinary catheter drained. It was a deep smoky red. I knew what that meant: trouble, bad trouble! The red color was hemoglobin, the oxygen-carrying substance in red blood cells. The fact that the urine was clear, although deeply colored, meant that toxins from the clostridial bacilli were breaking open the red blood cells and spilling hemoglobin into the bloodstream. The kidneys were then filtering it into the urine. Hemoglobin is toxic to the kidneys. The combination of low blood pressure and free hemoglobin can quickly destroy the kidneys.

But there were more immediate concerns. Our patient was now going into shock that did not respond to blood transfusions or to powerful medications to support the blood pressure. We could almost see the gas bubbles slowly spreading outward. It was an inexorable tidal wave of unbelievably vicious germs, destroying every normal cell in its path. The toxic breakdown products of the dead and dying cells were spilling out into the bloodstream. There they were breaking down the red blood cells. They were also dilating blood vessels so that they could no longer maintain the blood pressure.

I drew an even wider circle, extending now well up on to the abdomen. I toyed with the idea of a surgical mad dash, trying quickly to cut away all the dead and dying tissue and removing the invading organisms before the situation became hopeless. But in my heart, I knew that the situation was already hopeless. The pulse rate, which had been quite rapid, was slowing now to an ominous degree, one usually signaling imminent cardiac arrest. The heart, straining to maintain the circulation while bombarded with toxins, was beginning to fail.

"I can't get a blood pressure," said the anesthesiologist. ... No surprise. ... I gave up any thought of surgical heroics. This infection was more rapid and more powerful than any I had ever seen. It was winning its battle despite all we could do. It was claiming the patient's life while we watched. We had made the diagnosis of a rare disease promptly, and we had gotten to the OR only a few hours after the patient was first admitted. But we were too late.

From that point on, the patient's course was predictable and quick. His heart struggled briefly to maintain his life, despite being perfused with ever-increasing toxins from the dead and dying tissue. The heart rate got slower and slower and finally stopped beating altogether. Nothing we could do restored the beat. The planned operation never began. The patient was pronounced dead in the operating room.

Nobody said much. The nurses started to clean up the room. The intravenous lines and the urinary catheter were removed. The body was covered with a sheet and wheeled on a gurney to a service elevator and taken down to the basement morgue. I had a feeling of emptiness and awe and personal failure.

All my professional life in surgery, I never got over the feeling of awe I felt whenever a patient died in the operating room, sometimes right under my hands. There is such an awful finality. One moment there is life in the body, the next moment it is gone. Often there is also, however irrational, a feeling of guilt. How could I have saved this life? Could I have done anything differently? And usually you are painfully aware that family members are in the waiting room. You have to go out and share your unwelcome news, usually to the accompaniment of tears and sobbing. It's a bad scene.

I went alone to my office that day and simply sat at my desk for a long time. I was shaken by the whole episode. I needed time to settle myself before I went home to play with my children that Sunday afternoon. Their lives were just beginning, and they were full of energy. They radiated health and future promise. But I was fresh from witnessing the abrupt and frightening end of a life.

Reflecting on the day brought many strange thoughts to my mind. I couldn't stop thinking about the infection itself, starting with those telltale little bubbles of gas under the skin that I had first noticed when the patient was on the medical floor. I was shocked by the rapidity with which they seemed to multiply and spread. I wondered if they were continuing to grow and spread even now in the dead body. Clostridial bacilli thrive on dead tissue. What would the undertaker find? Would he race to perfuse the corpse with embalming fluid quickly? Would that kill the germs? What happens to all the dead bodies that we bury in handsome caskets? Are they full of germs and putrefaction? I tried to put those unpleasant thoughts out of my mind, but I still wondered what the funeral director would find.

My thoughts turned to the patient. I didn't know much about him. I knew that he was an insulin-dependent diabetic, a heavy smoker, and almost certainly an alcoholic. Those were the relevant medical facts I had elicited, but I knew virtually nothing of him as a person. He seemed to be one of those lost souls that we saw not infrequently, a drifter seeking temporary respite from a hard life in a VA hospital. Why was no next of kin listed, I thought. Did no one care about this man? Or did he simply not list a family member or friend? And why did I not sort this all out before going to surgery? I always tried to contact the next of kin before an emergency operation, why didn't I go out of my way to get a contact in this case? Was I, perhaps subconsciously, discriminating against the man because he seemed to be a drifter? Was my desire to have Sunday dinner with my wife and my children greater than my sense of responsibility to this patient? And I thought how sad it was for any life to end like this. No family, no friends interested and involved in his care. Cared for, in fact, by people who knew nothing about him personally, and who perhaps didn't even care to know. What had his life amounted to, anyway? I hoped that he had had some good times along the way that led to this sad end.

And I was struck, as I had been many times before, by how uncertain life can be. This man had presumably been in his usual state of health until a day or two before. He administered his usual dose of insulin in the front of his thigh. Somehow rare and incurable germs were introduced into his body with the insulin.

Perhaps he was thoughtless and careless with his sterile precautions. Perhaps he was drinking heavily. Perhaps he was deliberately careless, hoping that a minor infection might be his ticket to a VA hospital admission and three hot meals a day. Whatever the reason, his life was abruptly pulled from his grasp, despite our efforts.

Sobered, I changed clothes and headed home. I forced a few smiles and tried to get into a happier mood by playing board games with my children. I was glad that they had no idea of how I had spent my day.

This all happened 50 years ago. But even after half a century, I still have vivid memories of that patient. I can close my eyes and still feel the bubbles under his skin. I can still remember marking out those ever-expanding areas for surgical excision, hoping to get beyond the rapidly spreading infection, only to see it creep inexorably beyond my farthest marks. I can still see the dark red urine in the bag. I still wonder why his life should have ended in such a lonely and pathetic way, while I stood by, watching helplessly, in awe of the unrelenting force and speed with which those deadly bacteria did their work.

Death had chosen his agents well. They would not be denied. There was nothing I could do but admit that my best efforts were futile. It was not a good feeling.

At that time in my career, I regarded death as the ultimate enemy. And I had lost the battle in this patient. Looking back now, and remembering his dismal life circumstances, I wonder if he felt death was a blessing.

CHAPTER 11

Unexpected Outcomes

—

Early in my surgical training, one of the patients assigned to my resident team was a middle-aged woman with terminal breast cancer. Her disease had spread to her liver, lungs, and bones. She was in constant pain. Her body was emaciated. Her wrinkled skin showed that she had lost a lot of weight. And, despite her obvious need for emotional support, she seemed to be alone with her disease as she approached her death. We never saw any family, friends, or visitors at her bedside. Most of the time, she lay curled up on her side in a fetal position, eyes closed, occasionally moaning softly because of pain.

She was on the ward service for those patients with no money to pay for their care. The resident staff, particularly the chief resident, took care of these patients. A different staff surgeon was assigned each month to consult on problem cases and to assist in surgery if needed. The chief resident responsible for this particular patient was Dick Steenberg. Prematurely bald, tall, and self-assured, with piercing dark eyes, he was a bright and well-qualified young surgeon; but he was primarily interested in patients with challenging clinical problems that required major operations. A dying woman with a hopeless outlook and no family member even interested was not likely to get a lot of his time. From his point of view, her early death would be a blessing. And it would be a convenience to him and his staff.

So, on Dr. Steenberg's orders, we moved this pathetic woman into an inconspicuous corner bed of Ward D-Main, our women's charity ward. We kept the bedside curtains pulled tight around her bed. Perhaps it gave her some privacy, but mainly it protected the other patients from seeing a frightening reminder of their own mortality.

As for treatment of her cancer, there was nothing to offer at that time. Dick had us discontinue all drugs, except morphine, which was to be given in any amount necessary to control pain without concern as to any complications possible from morphine over-dosage, even respiratory depression leading to death. Food and drink were allowed, but only if the patient asked for them. This seemed unlikely, since she had resisted any efforts by the nurses to feed her or to help maintain an adequate fluid intake. In short, our exclusive clinical focus was to be pain relief by large doses of morphine. There was to be no further effort to treat the underlying disease or to prolong the patient's life. In fact, most of us agreed with Dick that the best outcome for this patient would be a peaceful early death, hopefully free of pain. So we settled back to wait for this unfortunate woman to die. Soon, we hoped.

It didn't happen that way. After a few days, she began to look more alert. She complained less of pain. She even asked for food. We were quite surprised, especially as her recovery continued day after day. After a few more days, Dr. Steenberg ordered a chest X-ray to see what was happening to the lung metastases. To our amazement, they were shrinking. Further X-rays showed that the bone metastases were also shrinking. And the patient improved clinically as well. She ate better and was able to walk without assistance. We were amazed. We saw no logical explanation for her dramatic improvement. After a while, there was no reason to keep her in the hospital any longer. She was discharged and continued to do well on clinic follow-up for some months, after which time I was on a different clinical rotation and lost track of her.

If we had given the poor woman any medication, we would have assumed that it was responsible for her improvement. But we had given her no medication at all, except morphine. Not even a shot of penicillin. We had no explanation for her remarkable return from the brink of death. It seemed like a miracle.

I didn't believe in miracles. I still don't. But I have seen other patients recover in a way that seemed miraculous at the time and later turned out to have an unsuspected scientific explanation. Such must have been the case with this woman as well. I'm sure some scientific reason explains her dramatic recovery. My favorite hypothesis was destruction of the adrenal glands by tumor.

Cancer sometimes spreads to the adrenal glands. Both glands can be completely destroyed. This leads to lack of the hormones produced by the adrenals. Some of these hormones stimulate the growth of breast cancer.

A few years after our patient's remission, there was a brief period when removing both adrenal glands in patients with widespread breast cancer came into vogue. In favorable patients, this procedure sometimes led to dramatic remissions, not unlike the one experienced by our earlier patient. Was this the cause of her remission?

I simply don't know. But I believe there is some rational explanation.

A few years later, circa 1962, when I was a young chief of surgery at the West Roxbury VA Hospital, I took care of another patient with an unexpected remission of late-stage cancer. He was a middle-aged man we operated on for stomach cancer. Unfortunately, his tumor was inoperable, having infiltrated pretty much the entire stomach and invaded the surrounding tissues. It had also spread to the lymph glands and liver. We took biopsies that showed an aggressive cancer that typically causes death within a few months. Surgery, X-ray therapy, and the chemotherapy of that time had nothing to offer. So we sent him home to die.

Two years later, the patient was doing well. He had had no treatment of any kind. We reviewed the pathology slides and found no change in the diagnosis or the expected outcome. We were puzzled but felt that if we understood more about this patient, it might help us treat other patients better. We readmitted him to the hospital and carried out a complete clinical evaluation. It showed that the stomach cancer was still present but had shrunk considerably. Some liver metastases had completely disappeared. We found no apparent explanation for the improvement.

At that time, our surgical team included a particularly bright young resident named Steve Rosenberg. Steve was headed for a distinguished career in surgical research. He had both MD and PhD degrees. He had an inquisitive mind, and he was quite intrigued by this patient, whose body seemed to be winning its struggle against a particularly aggressive cancer. Steve came up with a theory. He postulated that the patient's immune system had learned how to make antibodies against the cancer. He further postulated that if we could transfer antibodies from this patient to another patient with the same cancer, the second patient might also improve.

Steve scouted around and found another patient with incurable stomach cancer. He requested my permission to transfuse the second patient with blood from the first patient. Luckily, they were the same blood type. So, with the understanding and consent of both patients, the transfusion was carried out. (Today, permission for such unorthodox human experimentation would require the approval of an institutional review board.)

I would like to say that the second patient improved, but nothing happened. Nothing, that is, except that it whetted Steve's enthusiasm for studying the immune therapy of cancer. He went on to a distinguished career, ultimately becoming chief of surgery at the National Cancer Institute. (He briefly recounts this story in his autobiography, *The Transformed Cell*.) Both of these patients, and many others, made me realize how difficult it is to predict the outcome in cancer patients. I saw the folly of doing so, especially the folly and unkindness of taking away all hope.

Another patient I cared for about this time at the VA hospital was William Halloran, a man in his late sixties with colon cancer. He was the father-in-law of John Sheehan, our hospital director, who naturally took a close interest in his care. When I came out of the OR after operating on Mr. Halloran, John and his wife were sitting in the waiting room, anxious to know the outlook.

First, the good news, I thought: The operation

to remove the colon cancer had gone well. I expected a speedy and uneventful recovery. Now, the bad news: We found that the cancer had spread to the liver. The operation would not be a cure. They pressed for more details. How much longer does he have, Doctor? They were insistent. Reluctantly, I said that the average survival of colon cancer with liver metastases was about one year. The family was dismayed. I felt badly for them and for Mr. Halloran. But my estimate of his survival outlook was in line with that time.

Five years later, at his annual visit, Mr. Halloran was still doing well. He met the definition of a five-year cure—much to my surprise and to the family's delight. At each follow-up visit, I was gently but firmly reminded of my gloomy prediction of his short life expectancy. After Mr. Halloran's unexpectedly long survival, I learned to always tell patients and families about the "bell-shaped curve" of patient survival.

If a graph of disease mortality is plotted against time, the data will show that a few patients die early in their disease. As time goes by, more die each year until a peak is reached, after which the number of deaths declines each year. A few patients may live a long time. With some cancers, a very few never die of their disease. On a graph that plots time vs. mortality, this results in a bell-shaped curve. In practice, it means that you can't predict the life expectancy of any given patient with certainty.

Unpredictable circumstances can alter where a given patient fits on the curve. A dramatic example was Nancy Dunphy, the wife of one of my early surgical teachers. Dr. J. Englebert (Bert) Dunphy was one of the most distinguished American surgeons of the 20th century. He was a professor of surgery and department chair at Harvard, the University of Oregon, and the University of California, San Francisco. He was president of the most prestigious surgical societies and mentor to many future leaders of American surgery. He was also a great storyteller with a wicked sense of humor. Naturally, he was much in demand as a keynote speaker at major meetings and a visiting professor at many medical schools.

J. Englebert "Bert" Dunphy MD: a senior Peter Brent Brigham Hospital surgeon who dealt with many cancer deaths, both in his practice and in his personal life
Credit: Aesculapiad (Harvard Medical School Yearbook 1949)

When I was just starting the new Department of Surgery at the University of Massachusetts Medical School, I invited Dr. Dunphy to come for a week as a visiting professor. I thought it would give our young residents and faculty a lift, a sense that they were part of a significant surgical program, one that could attract a surgeon of Dr. Dunphy's stature to visit and participate in its activities. I crossed my fingers and hoped that he would accept the invitation.

Later, I learned that he had been undergoing

extensive treatment for prostate cancer. Nevertheless, he agreed to come and seemed glad to do so. I invited him and his wife Nancy to stay in our home, and I spent much of the week with them. I heard a great deal about his cancer and the distressing complications of his treatment. His major lecture was about care of the cancer patient, especially the human needs. I was probably the only one present who knew that Bert was talking about his own needs, as well as those of cancer patients in general. What I did not know was that he was talking about the needs of his wife Nancy as well.

A few years later, a close friend of the Dunphys told me Nancy's story. She had breast cancer. She had actually developed the disease several years before Bert developed prostate cancer. By the time of his diagnosis, she had advanced disease with widespread bone metastases. Her life expectancy was less than a year. But despite her own advanced disease, Nancy felt a great need to care for Bert. She told her closest friends: *I can't die! I have to take care of Bert. He needs me. I can't die.*

And she didn't die. The breast cancer nodules that had spread to her lungs, liver, and bones did not disappear on X-ray. There was no miraculous healing. But the metastases stopped growing. It was as though Nancy's desire to care for Bert was greater than the cancer's need to grow.

Bert's cancer was slowly progressive. Despite aggressive surgery, super-voltage radiotherapy, and chemotherapy, he went slowly downhill. After nine years, he died. During all that time, Nancy was by his side, comforting and caring for him. Her own disease was arrested in its development, not because of any new treatment, but because of her own fierce need to be healthy enough to care for Bert. For nine years she remained in remission.

With Bert's death, Nancy lost her main reason for living. Within three months, there was X-ray evidence of progression of the breast cancer. The progression was rapid. Within six months, Nancy was dead.

I have had patients who, like Nancy, seemed able to prolong their fatal illness until they could accomplish some cherished life goal—perhaps to attend a daughter's wedding, or be there for one more family Christmas, or finish some important task. Sometimes the willpower of the patient seemed stronger than the statistically predicted role of the disease. How a person's willpower can work this way, I have no idea. I wish I did. But I am glad that a person's willpower can sometimes influence their illness. I have always been glad that Nancy was able to overrule her own expected fate—an early death from breast cancer—to care for Bert during the nine years of his cancer treatment.

The message I learned from these and many other patients is this: *Never take away someone's hope.* At the same time, it is important to be realistic and to encourage advance planning for any outcome. It is a tricky balance. Like many other physicians, I learned from experience to advise patients to plan for the worst but hope for the best.

CHAPTER 12

Hints of a Hereafter

—

In the fall of 1955, I was a junior surgical resident at the West Roxbury VA Hospital, a teaching hospital affiliated with Harvard Medical School. I was just resuming my surgical training after two years in the U.S. Army Medical Corps. I had lots to learn about how the hospital functioned, including its emergency call system. It would be several years before doctors routinely carried pocket pagers or cellphones.

The emergency call system used a mixture of flashing lights and raucous beeps. Just below the ceiling on every floor, a tall, slender light box displayed a long column of lighted numbers. A red light at the bottom flashed only for emergencies. A loudspeaker produced either a soft, repetitive beep or a loud, attention-grabbing blast. Each doctor on call had an assigned number; mine was 27. When I was needed somewhere, the number 27 would flash on the light box, along with a series of soft beeps to get my attention. I would then check with the surgical nursing station or call the switchboard operator to find out where I was needed.

Life-and-death emergencies were rare but more dramatic: A loud, repetitive blast sounded like a fire truck racing to a fire, and the red light at the bottom of the light box would flash alarmingly. Rather than the doctor's number, the box displayed a number that indicated the location of the emergency. The first number indicated the floor of the hospital. The second number indicated the position on the floor: east wing, center, west wing. Any doctor in the hospital was expected to go immediately to the location of the emergency.

I was on duty one evening when the alarm went off for a life-and-death emergency. The number 12 was flashing, but it made no sense to me. The first floor, indicated by 1, had no patient services. The 2 indicated the center, which was front entrance and lobby.

Still, the alarm signal was clear: *Life-and-death emergency in the hospital lobby! Go there immediately!*

Because the elevators were notoriously slow, I raced down five flights, two and three steps at a time. When I burst into the lobby, I found about a dozen people, all in street clothes, crowded around the crumpled figure of a man lying inert on the floor. His face was deathly pale. I was the only person dressed in a white hospital uniform. It was obvious that I should do something, but I hardly knew what to do. Cardiopulmonary resuscitation (CPR) had not yet been invented. Almost by reflex, I pulled out my stethoscope and listened over his heart. Nothing. Not a sound. I knew intuitively that, no matter how long I listened, I would never hear a heartbeat. The man had died.

I remembered vaguely that I had read somewhere about a golfer who suffered a cardiac arrest after being struck by lightning. He had been brought back to life when his caddy made a fist and hit him directly over the heart with all his force. I had no idea how the caddy knew to do this or why it worked. But there on the lobby floor, surrounded by a circle of unknown outside bystanders, I had no idea what else to do. So I hauled off and hit the man directly over the heart, just as hard as I could. And for good measure, I hit him a second time as well, even harder.

Hardly daring to hope, I listened over his heart again. There was a regular beat! I could hardly believe my ears. And the man was returning to life. His eyelids were fluttering and color was coming back to his cheeks.

By this time, a medical resident had appeared. I asked him to arrange admission to the Medical ICU for cardiac monitoring, and I told the small crowd of onlookers to stand back out of the way. The patient was struggling to sit up and trying to speak. I put my hands on his shoulders, gently held him down on the floor and told him to lie quietly until orderlies arrived with a gurney to wheel him to the ICU. All I could think of was getting him out of the hospital lobby, with all its bystanders, and up to the ICU with its monitoring equipment, emergency supplies, and nursing staff. But all the patient could think of was some ineffable, transcendental, ethereal, truly awesome, and totally overwhelming experience that he had just been through. The expression on his face was like nothing I had ever seen before. Awe and joy and wonder and excitement were all mixed together, as well as a profound sense of peace. And he was anxious to tell us all about his experience. Words were jumbled up: *You can't imagine how beautiful. You'll never believe what I've seen. Let me tell you, please let me tell you! They were there, all of them. Wonderful! Incredibly beautiful! Please let me tell you!*

What was so beautiful, I wondered. Who was there? Where were they? I had never seen anyone so awestruck and yet so joyful as this freshly resuscitated patient. All I could say was: Later. You can tell us later. Please lie still. When we get you upstairs, then we can talk.

But when we finally got him into the Medical ICU, I never had the chance to talk to him about what he had seen. A senior cardiac fellow and a senior medical resident assumed responsibility, and before long an attending cardiologist arrived and took charge. As a junior surgical resident, I was not part of the team, even though I had been first on the scene and was lucky enough to restart the heart. However, I couldn't get the image of that transfigured face out of my mind, nor the fragments of his experience that he was trying so desperately to tell me about.

I did find out more of the patient's background. The man was not a veteran or a visitor. He was an entertainer. He played the piano in a small jazz combo that had been scheduled to entertain patients and visitors in our auditorium. He had walked up a flight of outside stairs, entered the front door, and collapsed on the lobby floor. The switchboard operator had seen the man fall to the floor and immediately flashed the emergency signal. Her rapid action, plus my sprint down the stairs, must have put me on the scene in less than a minute, fortunately for the piano player.

The cardiologists ultimately determined that the man had underlying heart disease and later he had successful open-heart surgery to correct the problem.

After he had been in the ICU a few days, my curiosity got the better of me. I kept seeing that awestruck, joyous face. And I wanted to know what he had been so anxious to tell me about. So I went down to the

MICU, feeling a bit uncomfortable because I knew the staff might wonder just who I was and whether or not I was entitled to visit a patient on the critical list. I hoped that my white coat might serve as a ticket of admission to the restricted area. And it did.

But there was an unexpected problem. Although I had saved his life, he didn't remember me. And he was tired of being interviewed or examined by what must have seemed to him like an endless succession of young doctors in white coats. The man who had been so euphoric and bubbling over to tell me about his ecstatic and remarkable experience now was reluctant to talk, especially about otherworldly visions that strangers might regard as delusions or fantasies or hallucinations. Realizing that I was now a stranger to him, I became shy about posing any probing questions, especially about profound but deeply personal experiences. I came away disappointed, knowing only that he had had a transcendental vision that he really didn't want to share with an inquisitive young stranger.

I had never heard of a near-death experience, and I doubt that the patient had either. It would be 20 years before the phenomenon would be made widely known by Dr. Raymond Moody in a bestselling book called *Life After Life*. Prospective studies done later by Dr. Kenneth Ring, a University of Connecticut psychologist, helped validate the experience. Many other books also described near-death experiences. In retrospect, I am sure that the man resuscitated by a blow on the chest had such an experience.

By the time that I saw my next patient with a near-death experience, over two decades later, I had heard of the phenomenon from several other patients and other physicians. I was no longer an inexperienced resident too timid to ask probing questions; I was the chief of surgery at the new University of Massachusetts (UMass) Hospital and an experienced surgeon with much closer rapport with my patients. I was much better equipped to probe an esoteric experience when the right patient came along. As it turned out, the right patient was Thelma Z. But when I first saw her, I tried my best to refer her to some other surgeon. She looked like trouble, the most anxious patient I had ever seen. I wondered: *Why is she so nervous? She looks scared to death. Why is she so upset?*

Thelma Z was about 60, but she reminded me of a 16-year old girl seeing a surgeon for the first time, afraid to undress and be examined, much less to be put to sleep and undergo surgery. But her medical problem didn't seem to warrant her great anxiety. She had gallstones, a common and relatively nonthreatening medical condition, at least in my eyes. She was a plump, middle-aged housewife with gray-brown hair, brown eyes, and thick eyeglasses. I saw nothing distinctive about her appearance.

I was surprised to be seeing a patient with gallstones. I hadn't done any gallbladder surgery for some years, having limited my practice to vascular surgery. I usually referred any patients with gallbladder disease to other surgeons. She was self-referred to me at her own insistence. My secretary had tried to refer Mrs. Z to some other surgeon, but the patient had insisted—quite emphatically—on seeing me. After two or three calls, I finally agreed to see her, thinking that I could convince her to be cared for by another surgeon.

Why was she so determined to see me? I asked her the question directly, but at first she was reluctant to tell me. Only after I was on the brink of refusing to care for her did the full story come out. And when it did, I changed my mind about caring for her.

Several weeks before, she had suffered sudden and severe abdominal pain associated with nausea, vomiting, and a fever. She had been admitted to Worcester Memorial Hospital, an excellent community hospital. The doctor made a diagnosis of an acute gallbladder attack. After receiving pain medications, intravenous fluids, and antibiotics, she improved.

An ultrasound study confirmed the presence of gallstones. Surgery was strongly advised, but the patient refused. She had a powerful premonition that if she were operated upon at that hospital, she would die. Because she did not consider herself to be at all superstitious, she was surprised at how powerful this premonition was. She did not tell the surgeon who was caring for her. She was afraid he would think it was silly. He continued to press for an operation. She continued to refuse. She finally signed herself out of the hospital, against medical advice.

However, the pain did not go away. It would wax and wane, but at times it became quite severe. She knew that the surgeon was right, but she still had the gut feeling that if she underwent surgery there, she would die. Irrational as she knew this feeling was, she could not manage to shake it.

Distraught and still in pain, she decided to consider being operated on by a different surgeon in a different hospital. She was a highly intelligent woman and approached making this decision as a life-or-death matter.

She went to the Worcester Public Library to study a copy of the *Directory of Medical Specialists*, which contains short biographies of surgeons across the country. She carefully read about the professional background and credentials of all the surgeons in central Massachusetts. She was reassured as she read my write-up, though I'm not quite sure why. She became convinced that if I operated on her, she would live and be well; but if anyone else operated on her, she would die. I was not flattered by her confidence in me. She was not the sort of patient I looked forward to caring for. Her anxiety almost certainly meant that a lot of time would be spent reassuring her. Also, because I have had a few patients in whom such premonitions proved true, I had said to myself that I was never going to operate on another patient with a death premonition.

And now here I was with Thelma Z, who had just dramatically described the strongest premonition of death I had ever encountered. But there was a twist. An important twist. In her premonition, she was convinced she would live if I did the operation. It was almost as though I would condemn her to die if I refused to do the surgery. I did not like to be put in that position, but finally, against my better judgment, I agreed to operate. She was very grateful but still quite nervous. So was I.

The day of surgery arrived, and the operation was uneventful. Her postoperative condition was excellent, and she was sent to the surgical ward. I told her husband that all was well. I was quite relieved to have the surgery over and the patient in good condition. But the story wasn't over.

I saw Thelma Z on afternoon rounds. All seemed well. Her state of mind, her blood pressure, temperature, heart rate, urine output, breathing, pain control: all were in good order. That evening, though, I got a call from the surgical resident on call. On routine post-op checkup, he had been listening to her heart and had heard a skipped beat or two, a momentary cardiac rhythm disturbance. Not all that unusual, really. Some patients have skipped heartbeats from time to time, with no symptoms and no ill effects. Still, it was a slightly worrisome occurrence in this particular patient.

I had told the resident at the time of surgery about the death premonition and the patient's anxiety. So he was more concerned about skipped heartbeats than he might have been otherwise. He had transferred her to the Surgical Intensive Care Unit so that her heart rate could be monitored continuously through the night. As it turned out, that simple decision to transfer her saved Thelma Z's life.

About two am, the alarm signifying a cardiac arrest suddenly went off at her bedside. Nurses rushed in when *CODE BLUE, SICU* blared from loudspeakers. Emergency buzzers assigned to surgeons, anesthesiologists, and cardiologists went off in on-call rooms nearby. Within less than a minute, ICU nurses had started chest massage. Within another minute, an endotracheal tube was in place, and the anesthesiologist on call was breathing the patient by squeezing a rubber bag attached to the tube. Electric current through chest paddles restarted the heart, and everyone began to relax. Resuscitation had begun; the patient was responding. All the necessary personnel were on hand.

The cardiologist passed a thin wire up through an arm vein into the heart and hooked it up to an external pacemaker. If the heart's own nerve conduction broke down again, the pacemaker would immediately stimulate the heart to beat at a normal rate. Everything was under control. The crisis had passed. The breathing tube was removed, and the room tidied up. Now the SICU staff could deal with second-order priorities, such as notifying me and the husband, both far from the scene of battle.

When the telephone woke me from a sound sleep, I could hardly believe what had happened. With no advance warning, my patient had suffered a near-fatal cardiac arrest. Fortunately, she had survived, thanks only to the fact that, unlike most patients after routine gallbladder operations, she had been monitored in a high-tech ICU with a highly trained response team immediately available. Her premonition had been right. She would almost certainly have died if managed as a routine gallbladder patient in a different hospital environment.

As I rushed to the hospital, I imagined that I would find her hysterical. Knowing how anxious and frightened she had been pre-operatively, I assumed that, after a full-blown resuscitation, she would be totally distraught. I braced myself for the scene that I was sure would follow.

But when I got to the bedside, Thelma Z was the most relaxed and peaceful person in the ICU. Her face was tranquil. Her manner was calm. I stared in amazement, surprised and grateful, not saying a word. I wondered if the anesthesiologist had given her a strong sedative.

"Dr. Wheeler," she began slowly, "I know one thing

for sure … I'll never be afraid of death again."

"Why not?"

"I can't believe what happened to me. I suddenly found myself floating near the ceiling, looking down at my body in the bed. An alarm was going off. Nurses rushed over. One said, 'There's been no QRS for 45 seconds.' Another started pumping up and down on my chest. Hard! … Dr. Wheeler, what's a QRS?"

"It shows the heartbeat on an EKG, Thelma. Go on, what happened next?"

And so she went on. Her story was quite remarkable, but her manner was even more remarkable to me. She was transformed by her experience. Gone was the anxious, apprehensive, agitated manner I had seen so much of during my contacts with her. The experience had transformed her. She was totally at peace. Even death held no fear for her.

She described quite accurately the resuscitation attempts. Later, I verified her account with the ICU staff. It tallied exactly, even the comment about "no QRS for 45 seconds."

But the resuscitation was only part of the experience, and not the most impressive part at that. She described a beautiful parklike place where relatives long dead welcomed her. I no longer remember the details, but I will never forget how reassuring it was to her and how totally at peace she was with the idea of an afterlife. We had not discussed such things before, but I had the strong impression that she previously had not believed in an afterlife. Rather death had seemed like total annihilation, a thought she found terrifying.

During the rest of her hospital course, Thelma Z

maintained her equanimity. It turned out that she had a rare conduction problem in the nerves that trigger the heartbeat. A permanent pacemaker was implanted, and she lived for many years thereafter. I have often wondered where that life-saving premonition came from.

I never asked her further about the near-death experience. I don't know why I didn't. Perhaps I thought it was a private matter and that I would be invading her privacy. Or perhaps it was simply one of those unexpected things in life that don't fit neatly into our usual belief system, so we leave them unexamined rather than threaten a comfortable status quo. Some years later, when near-death experiences became more widely discussed in public, I developed much more curiosity about their significance. I talked to other patients who described their past near-death experiences to me in some detail, but without the rapturous, transformative expression that I had seen on the faces of the VA piano player and Thelma Z immediately after their experiences. Certainly it was an enormously reassuring experience for them, and perhaps for me as well.

Loss of the fear of death is one of the most prominent characteristics of the near-death phenomenon. I was particularly struck by that loss of fear with Thelma Z, since she had such a paralyzing fear of death before her near-death experience. I had trouble believing her account of an out-of-body experience. She vividly described floating up near the ceiling and looking down at her body while the resuscitation was going on.

But in what form was she floating above her body? Certainly no form that the nursing staff could see. And how was she "seeing" the scene? The patient's eyes were closed. Her heart wasn't beating. So it is doubtful that she could have seen anything with her own eyes, even if her eyelids had been open. And if her eyes were open and seeing, they would have been looking up at the ceiling, not down at her body. How could she possibly have been looking down at her body and observing her resuscitation quite accurately? How can you see without eyes? Still, her experience of floating up near the ceiling and looking down at her own body has been a fairly typical component of many other near-death experiences, as I learned later.

Out-of-body experiences are not uncommon in well-documented near-death situations. I read about a dramatic case report in the spring 2010 issue of my Harvard medical alumni magazine. Dr. Allan Hamilton, an Arizona neurosurgeon, tells the story of Sarah, a woman who underwent life-threatening surgery to repair a brain aneurysm.

Because the aneurysm was in a dangerous location at the base of the brain, it was necessary to temporarily stop the heart and shut off circulation to the brain. Before shutting off the circulation, it was necessary to cool the body down to the point that there were no brain waves and no other evidence of brain function. The patient was clinically dead. Nevertheless, during that time when the heart was not beating and the blood was not circulating and there was no evidence of any brain function, Sarah saw and heard what was going on in the operating room. She could describe the scene in detail, later verified by the OR staff and the recording monitors. She could report even casual remarks by the anesthesiologist and the OR staff about a nurse's marriage proposal the previous evening and the size of her engagement ring.

A year or two before reading this story, I watched a British Broadcasting Company TV documentary on the near-death experience. It highlighted a similar case report. That patient also had a deep-seated brain aneurysm and underwent surgical repair with the heart stopped and the body drastically cooled to protect the brain. No brain waves were recorded, but the patient was able to see and hear what went on in the OR and report it accurately. She also had visions of going into an afterlife where she was reunited with dead relatives and friends. She found that afterlife so wonderful that she had to be forced to return to Earth by a dead uncle, someone to whom she had been particularly close before his death.

On the BBC program, one case of particular interest to me was of a woman who had been blind since birth. During the near-death experience, she could see things that she had never seen before. It was a revelation to her to see objects and people that she had known only by touch. Unfortunately, after she survived the near-death experience, she was again blind. It was as though a form of consciousness was bottled up inside her; it was able to see when out of her physical body, but not when it was confined within her body.

In November 2012 the cover story of *Newsweek* magazine was about a remarkable and well-documented near-death experience, reported by Dr. Eben Alexander, a neurosurgeon who had been comatose for seven days due to a rare form of bacterial meningitis. He described his experience in convincing detail in his book *Proof of Heaven*.

Dr. Mary C. Neal, an orthopedic surgeon, also had a personal near-death experience that is described in her book *To Heaven and Back*. And there have been many other bestselling books on near-death experiences.

What does this all add up to? First of all, I have no doubt about the validity of the near-death experience. The shining, joyous, peaceful look on the face of Thelma Z (and the equally ecstatic face of the musician I had resuscitated at the VA hospital years before) could never have been faked. Their stories of a near-death experience ring true to me, and other patients of mine have described similar experiences that I did not witness personally. Many people have reported near-death experiences and been studied by reputable investigators. There is a point beyond which I cannot understand all the implications, and I do not care to try. What I am sure of is that the patients who have had these experiences have found them profoundly reassuring. They have lost their fear of death. They have had a beautiful vision of what might truly be an afterlife. And it is a vision of love and peace. I find it hopeful.

Steve Jobs, cofounder of the Apple computer company, died of cancer at the age of 56. Jobs changed many people's daily lives with his innovative Macintosh computers, iPhone, iPod, and iPad. When he died, the media were full of stories about him. One small press report caught my eye. It reported that at the very end, as his death approached, this hard-nosed inventor/CEO called out in surprise and excitement, "Oh, wow!" The expression seemed to be in response to whatever he saw at the moment of death. I wondered if Steve Jobs had a deathbed vision like patients with near-death experiences.

CHAPTER 13

A Big Win Becomes a Big Loss.

—

The West Roxbury VA Hospital had no emergency ward. On weekdays, a full-time VA physician evaluated patients for hospital admission. On nights and weekends, a resident evaluated any walk-in patients. On one Sunday afternoon in the early 1960s, a surgical resident was called to see a man who came to the admissions office. The patient brought a sealed envelope containing a letter from his personal physician.

The resident could see at a glance that the patient was severely ill. His skin color was the deep yellow-green of jaundice, due to bile duct obstruction. Even the whites of his eyes had become yellow. He was about 40 years old, medium height, and had the wrinkled skin of severe weight loss. The letter from his referring physician told a sad story. The patient's name was Tony L, a high-school teacher in nearby Framingham. He was married and had two small children. A year before, he had undergone a bowel resection for colon cancer. The operation showed that the tumor had already spread to the liver. After surgery the liver cancer grew rapidly, and the patient was referred now for terminal care.

While the resident was reading this letter, he was paged and had to leave the examining room for a few minutes. He returned to find an angry patient who said,

"I read the letter! I had no idea that I was being referred for terminal care! I don't want to die in this hospital. If I am going to die, I want to die at home." And he refused to talk about the matter. He left the hospital against medical advice.

Hearing this story, I could easily empathize with a man close to my own age, a man who had left our hospital to tell his wife and children that he had come home to die. We had failed him. There was no effective chemotherapy for colon cancer in the early 1960s. But I had heard that a new drug was under study and showed occasional benefit. The chemical name for the drug was *5-fluorouracil*, usually referred to as 5-FU. I wondered if Tony L might be a candidate for treatment with 5-FU. What did he have to lose?

So I called him and said, "My name is Brownell Wheeler, and I am a surgeon at the VA hospital. I was told by the doctor who saw you here yesterday that you had been referred for terminal care and that you refused. I have read recent medical reports about a new anti-cancer drug. With your permission, I would like to explore whether you might benefit or whether we could help in any other way. It would require you to come into the hospital for a few days."

"What are the chances the new drug will help?"

"I don't know. But we will find out as much as we can, and we will share all that information honestly with you. We will do our best to help, but I can't promise a miracle."

And so Tony L agreed to be admitted to the hospital for evaluation and possible treatment. In the meantime, I contacted cancer specialists who were studying 5-FU. They estimated a 20-percent chance of tumor regression. To Mr. L that chance seemed better than nothing, and he was started on daily intravenous 5-FU therapy. The situation was desperate, so we used the highest permissible dosage.

After several days, we saw encouraging signs. Blood tests of liver function showed improvement. His urine had been quite dark. Bile had backed up into the bloodstream, causing dark urine, pale stools, and jaundice. After several days of 5-FU treatment, the urine became lighter in color and the stools darker. The jaundice took longer to clear, but slowly his skin color returned to normal also. We were watching a miracle!

The 5-FU treatment was continued beyond the usual course. We wanted to maximize the effect of the drug. Fortunately, Tony had no adverse side effects, and he returned to near normal appearance. He even returned to teaching. On weekends he came into the hospital for intravenous infusions of 5-FU. After a year had passed, I presented him to Grand Rounds at the Peter Bent Brigham Hospital. The audience was amazed at this great clinical triumph over what had been regarded as a hope-less situation.

But the recovery was too good to last. Several weeks after the Grand Rounds presentation, I noticed that his liver was enlarging. The tumor was growing again. More 5-FU had no effect. Inexorably, the tumor progressed. Jaundice reappeared. He lost weight and strength. Finally, he was admitted for terminal care, two full years after he was first referred for that purpose. We did our best to make him comfortable. There was nothing more that we could do.

Shortly after Tony died, his wife came to pick up his belongings. She was quite unhappy, which was no surprise; but she also seemed angry, which was totally unexpected. Awkwardly, I tried to comfort her.

"I am so sorry that we couldn't save Tony," I said. "We tried our best. And at least we gave him another two years."

It was the wrong thing to say. She looked even more angry and said, "They were not good years, Dr. Wheeler. The cancer was always hanging over our heads. Tony often didn't feel well. We could never get any private time away together. Even on weekends, he had to come into the VA hospital for chemo. Tony told me he was sorry he ever walked into your hospital."

Her words were like a punch in my gut. I had expected her to be grateful for prolonging her husband's life for two full years. Instead, she blamed me for prolonging his suffering—and hers too. It hurt.

I said simply, "I'm sorry."

What more could I say?

I relived that conversation many times. I could not understand how state-of-the-art treatment that my colleagues and I regarded as a professional triumph could be seen as a personal tragedy by the patient and his wife.

There were hidden lessons for me to learn. With time, I realized that I had been looking at Tony's clinical decisions through my eyes, rather than through his. To me, the most important goal was prolonging his life. To Tony and his wife, what mattered most was preserving the quality of his life. If that was not possible, death was a blessing. He taught me that clinical decisions should be based on the patient's values, not mine. And that I should never assume that the patient shares my values. It was a lesson that I would learn again and again.

CHAPTER 14

The Gypsy King

—

Gus M didn't come to me by choice, either his or mine. Gus was swept into my vascular clinic by a tidal wave of family, close friends, and followers. Gus was in his sixties, dark-eyed, grim-faced, and bald except for a disheveled fringe of white hair. His restless dark eyes were quite alert, though, guardedly taking in the whole scene, apprehensive and faintly hostile.

Gus was a longtime, insulin-dependent diabetic and a chronic heavy smoker. His medical history included two heart attacks and three strokes, leaving him permanently paralyzed on the right, his dominant side, and completely unable to speak. Blood tests showed seriously impaired kidney function. His life expectancy was severely limited, and his quality of life was irrevocably impaired. However, his current medical problem was a painful right leg.

His leg had become red and painful two or three weeks earlier. His large family decided, quite correctly, that the leg looked like an ominous problem. And they felt that nothing but the best medical care would do for Gus. Although they lived in Worcester, they decided that, to get the best medical care, they should take Gus to the most prestigious medical center in Boston. In their minds, that was the Massachusetts General Hospital and its world-famous Harvard faculty.

I don't know exactly what happened when this unruly family went to MGH, but their patriarch obviously didn't receive the attention the family wanted for him. I doubt if they got by the security guards at the front door. So they went across Boston to the Beth Israel Hospital, another famous Harvard teaching hospital. The outcome there was not much better, but they did get to see a vascular surgeon, who referred them to me. He told them that there was nobody better able to care for the painful leg, that I had been a well-known Harvard vascular surgeon and that I now practiced much closer to where they lived. If anybody could save the leg, he said, it was Dr. Wheeler.

I did not appreciate the compliments and the referral. It was passing the buck, rather than a true compliment; and I saw at a glance that nobody could save Gus's leg.

The color of the foot and lower leg was a mixture of bright red and dark purplish blue. The purple color was due to blood that had leaked though tiny, oxygen-deprived blood vessels into the tissue. When I pressed the purplish areas with a finger, they did not blanch, as they would if the color had been due to swollen but still intact blood vessels. When damaged vessels let blood leak out into the tissues in this way, there is no going back. The red blood cells must be eliminated by the body's defenses, as with a bruise. However, if the underlying cause of the problem is not correctable, or if too much time has gone by without restoring blood flow, the purple turns to black: gangrene.

Gus could not feel a pinprick in that leg, suggesting that the nerves were badly damaged. In his case, though, there was another possible explanation for the nerve damage. Diabetes sometimes damages the sensory nerves to the feet and lower legs. In such patients, surgeons can often amputate a gangrenous toe or drain an abscess without anesthesia. Still, the inability to feel pain was a bad sign. There was also no muscle function. I was sure that his leg was beyond salvage.

Gus's family consisted of 12 to 15 people, mostly young adults, who all wanted to be in on the action. I tried to sort out who was in charge. A woman in her twenties kept pushing herself between the patient and me. She had long, dark hair, dark eyes, and dark skin with a trace of pockmarks. Her dress was colorful and tight. The taut fabric emphasized her large breasts.

I asked who she was.

"I am his daughter, Judith," she stated like a challenge, almost as if to say, *I am in charge here.*

However, I didn't want to deal with Judith. Her aggressiveness, youth, provocative dress, and body language all made me want to talk to someone else.

So I asked, "Is your mother here?" If I couldn't talk with the patient, I wanted to talk with his wife, the legal next of kin.

Judith pointed to an older woman on the fringe of the group, standing with two young men on either side of her. Her head and eyes were cast down. She looked totally out of place, ill at ease, and almost as unable to communicate as Gus. "She does not speak English," Judith said. I knew that I was stuck in having to deal with the daughter. I started, as gently as I knew how, to explain that the leg had been without blood supply for too long, that the damage was irreversible, and that an amputation was necessary. I wasn't sure she understood.

"You CAN save the leg, Doctor." Judith's declaration was almost a shout ... a command ... a direct order. "I KNOW you can!"

She pushed herself close to me, too close, her ample bust pressed firmly against my chest. She looked up directly into my eyes and said fiercely, "I know you can." She pressed her body still closer against mine, as though her physical force and her sexuality would somehow force me to do as she said.

Uncomfortable, I stepped back. I felt compromised, and I didn't like it.

"I don't think the leg can be saved," I said, "but he needs to come into the hospital regardless. I'll admit him, and we'll talk further later." With apprehension and misgivings, I fled the scene.

The nurses on 3 West, the surgical ward, were just as apprehensive as I was about caring for this patient. They told me the family was a clan of Roma. They said Gus was the "king." I tried not to be involved in the gossip. However, the people assembled around Gus were definitely unusual. And it was clear that no matter how disabled, Gus was still revered as the group's leader, almost an Old Testament patriarch if not truly a king.

Fortunately, the pain in his leg abated. The Roma clan gave me credit. I knew the truth was otherwise—and a bad sign. Dead tissue does not hurt; dying tissue hurts. When cells die, pain is relieved. A third-degree burn is not as painful as a first-degree burn. Gus' lower leg was dead. But the family didn't accept the obvious. They still hoped for a miracle. But I knew that I was not a miracle worker. I played for time so that the need for amputation—so obvious to me—could sink in on the patient and his whole clan. I felt pressure from the hospital administration not to waste a precious hospital bed on a hopeless situation, especially one where the hospital did not expect any reimbursement. Gingerly, I broached the question of amputation again. The suggestion caused an immediate uproar from the family, anguished cries and shouts of anger and denial. I decided to revisit the issue later.

A day or two later, with considerable difficulty, I cleared the room of everyone, except for Judith; her mother, the patient's wife, who seemed to have little comprehension of what was going on; and two young men usually present with the wife. I assumed that they were the patient's sons. They usually deferred to their sister Judith, but they clearly understood English and were obviously involved in any decision-making. I was determined to push for some resolution. The leg was turning black. It was clearly beyond salvage. Amputation seemed inevitable to me, and I saw no point in delaying the decision any longer.

Backed up by two surgical residents, a physician's assistant, and a nurse, I spoke directly to the patient. Although unable to speak, his bright, alert eyes seemed to show he understood what I was saying. As far as I could tell, he was mentally capable of making decisions for himself, and he had every legal and moral right to do so.

I spoke slowly and distinctly, pausing frequently to be sure that he understood what I was saying. "Gus, your leg is too far gone to save. ... In fact, the lower part of your leg is already dead. ... That is why you don't feel it

anymore—and even the pain you used to have is gone. ...
Sooner or later, it will get you into serious health problems. ... Since you are a diabetic, you are especially likely
to develop a serious infection or some other complication of diabetes. Some of those complications might
prove fatal. ... On the other hand, if we do an amputation
and remove the dead tissue, you will be in a stable situation and able to do whatever you were doing before you
developed the leg problem." I knew that because of the
stroke Gus was unable to walk and had been confined to
a wheelchair.

"So, I strongly recommend that you have an amputation very soon," I continued. "Otherwise, complications
could develop any time. ... There really is no option." I
paused to wait for his reaction. His face was getting red,
and his eyes looked at me angrily.

"He will never agree to that, Doctor," said his
daughter emphatically. "He only wants to go home."

"That's not very realistic. If he goes home, complications will probably develop before long. And he may
die if they are not treated promptly. I can't tell exactly
what may happen. I have never seen a patient who tried
to live at home despite a dead leg. If we send your dad
home in this condition, I can't be responsible for what
may happen. I think he could die."

"He only wants to go home," she repeated with
emphasis. "He will never agree to an amputation."

"Does he understand that he may die if he doesn't
have an amputation?"

She shrugged her shoulders. I turned back to the
patient. "Gus, do you understand that you may die if we
send you home without an amputation?" He nodded his

head affirmatively.

"Gus, I have to be sure that you know exactly what is at stake here. Do you want to stay in the hospital where we can do an amputation and get you healed and reasonably healthy? Or do you want to go home without an amputation and probably die before too long?"

Gus was obviously agitated: *Why is this doctor so dense? Why can't he understand?* With great effort, he raised himself on one elbow, paused, and then fixed his eyes steadily on me. There was a complete hush in the room. We were all waiting for whatever was coming next, and clearly the next move was his. Slowly, he opened his mouth and sucked in a great lungful of air. Then a primal sound exploded from the depths of his being: "*HHH-HOOOOMMMMME.*"

After that agonized explosion of sound, there was a dead silence. It was the first word he had spoken since the last stroke. And its meaning was clear. It was clear to his family, as well as to me, that Gus knew exactly what was involved. He was going home to die. After two heart attacks, three disabling strokes, insulin-dependent diabetes, a gangrenous leg, and God knows what other medical problems, he was going home for the last time.

Exhausted by his effort, Gus sank back on his pillow. For a moment, no one moved or said anything. There was nothing to say. Gus had taken charge of his life—and his eventual death—and nothing that any of us could say would matter. His family started filing slowly out of the room.

Judith grabbed my sleeve and pulled me to one corner of the room. Standing on tiptoe so she could speak directly into my ear, she whispered urgently, "You will come to our house and see him." It wasn't a request. Nor a polite question, such as, "Will you make a house call, Doctor?" It wasn't even a statement of fact. It was a command. And it had better be followed. There was an implied threat in her tone of voice: *You had better come see him, if you know what's good for you.*

And so, a couple of days later, I found myself searching for their house. The address given was one of the older and more rundown sections of Worcester. At one time, it had been primarily two- and three-story apartment buildings, side by side, with no yards or greenery to relieve the monotony of drab buildings. Over the years, some older buildings had been torn down and replaced by gas stations, convenience stores, pawnshop, and small commercial buildings. The address I was looking for turned out to be the second floor of an old two-story frame building next to a gas station. I entered a narrow, dark hall, slowly climbed a flight of wooden stairs, and knocked on the door.

Judith quickly answered the knock and ushered me into the living room. The curtains were drawn. Only a few candles lighted the room. Plaster statues of Catholic saints stood on the bureaus. Prominent on one wall was a crucifix with an agonized figure of Christ. On another wall, there was a picture of a gentle and kindly Christ, encircled by a crown of thorns and pointing to his bleeding heart. The room reminded me of a darkened side-chapel in an old European church. Somehow, I had never thought of this pushy, demanding, difficult group— so bitterly accused by our nurses of being burglars and thieves—as being religious. Religious iconography was a central part of their lives during this family crisis, at least for the women who appeared to run the house.

Stretched out on a couch, propped up into a half-sitting position by pillows, Gus looked much more comfortable than he had in the hospital. His expression was serene. He seemed at peace with his surroundings, quiet and in control. I wondered what purpose it served for me to be there. But I had brought the usual physician props and was prepared to play the part, for whatever it was worth: Count the pulse. Take the blood pressure. Feel the neck pulses and listen for murmurs. Tap out the heart borders and listen for murmurs or irregularities of the heartbeat. Tap out the chest and listen to the lungs. And so on.

Of course, the critical part of this exam was to check the bad leg. I was as curious as the family to see what was happening. I had never seen a patient who refused an amputation for a dying leg, so I had never watched the disease run its natural course. A loose stockinet bandage covered the gangrenous right leg. Carefully, I removed the dressing.

When I had last seen the leg, it had been a deep purplish blue from the foot up to just below the knee, where it changed to a reddish color that gradually faded out above the knee. The upper leg was normal. Now the lower leg was totally black. The red color above the knee was practically gone. The dead lower leg was clearly demarcating from the healthy tissue above. I saw no drainage or sign of infection. The lower leg was totally numb: Dead tissue doesn't hurt. I detected no distressing symptoms and no imminent crisis. I wondered how long this benign state of affairs could continue.

Judith pulled me out into the kitchen to see the

latest urine specimen. She dipped strips of specially treated paper into the clear yellow fluid. The color of the paper did not change, indicating there was no sugar or acetone present. With pride, she showed me a chart of such tests dating back to hospital discharge. The diabetes was under good control. The diet and the dose of insulin must be appropriate. She also showed me a record of the patient's temperature readings, all normal. She took great pride in her nursing care. I complimented her and left the house without a clue as to how this would all turn out. I was sorry that we had not done an amputation so that we could now have a stable situation. How can someone with severe diabetes have a dead leg and not expect trouble? Still, Gus seemed to be doing well so far.

Judith had made it apparent that she expected on-going visits. Nothing was ever said about paying me for a house call, and I didn't even bother to notify our billing clerk about my visits. I knew nothing would be paid, and I didn't much care.

Two or three days later, I made another house call. The living room was much brighter. Still no electric lights, but many more candles. And another couple of plaster saints. St. Francis had joined the scene, casting bread to the birds at his feet. And St. Christopher was now there, carrying the Christ child safely across a stream. Nothing else had changed. Gus was still lying comfortably propped up on a couple of pillows on the couch. The atmosphere seemed peaceful and serene. Gus was enjoying being the center of attention, and his family was enjoying being his caretakers. He was in no pain, and no medical crisis seemed to be on the horizon. The diabetes was still under control. No one seemed concerned about what the future might hold.

I went step by step through a brief physical examination, irrelevant, as it seemed to me under the circumstances. For me to play a familiar physician role was obviously reassuring to the family. So I went through the usual drill. Heart sounds, normal; breath sounds, clear; and so on. But when I removed the bandages, I saw the lower leg was now even darker black and shrunken. The skin had become tough and leathery. There wasn't any muscle. It reminded me of the shriveled leg of an Egyptian mummy. It could have been 3,000 years old.

What had happened to the breakdown products of the dead muscle? Surely some toxic cell components must have found their way into the bloodstream. Did they have no ill effects? I would have expected that the blood level of potassium might go up, for example. Muscle cells are rich in potassium. As the muscle cells died from lack of oxygen and the cell membranes broke down, potassium should have been released into the bloodstream. And high blood potassium can cause fatal rhythm disturbances of the heart, even in a healthy patient. Could a leg die and have no obvious ill effects on the rest of the body, even in Gus, a patient with heart disease, diabetes, and multiple other medical problems? How long could this go on? I left without knowing the answers.

And on the visits went, for three or four weeks more. Gus had gone home to die, but his guardian angels seemed in no hurry to take him back. On the other hand, I was more than ready to turn Gus over to their care. There wasn't much I could do, especially since Gus chose to ignore any medical advice.

As the days went by, Gus began sleeping more and

more. Gradually, he became more withdrawn and weaker physically. The lower leg had mummified. There was no drainage or other indication of infection. The leg did not seem to be the cause of his increasing lethargy. Just below the knee, a sharp line of demarcation had developed between the black, mummified lower leg and apparently healthy skin. The leg seemed stable, so I didn't think it could account for his clinical deterioration. Was it just his lack of exercise and his self-imposed bed rest? Or his expectation of an imminent and welcome death? Or was it some medical problem that I was overlooking?

My examinations became more thoughtful. One day, listening carefully to breath sounds in his back, I heard faint crackling sounds at the base of each lung. They suggested to me an early pneumonia or congestive heart failure or just a failure to ventilate the lung bases adequately because of prolonged inactivity and general weakness. His temperature was slightly elevated for the first time. Ordinarily, in these circumstances I would have ordered a chest X-ray and some blood tests. However, taking Gus back to the hospital was not something to undertake lightly. Besides, he would almost certainly refuse to go. And perhaps this new chest finding—whatever its cause—was simply nature taking its course, one which the patient might welcome. He might be angry at any attempt to intervene.

I decided there was little point in discussing all the possibilities with the family. I knew only too well how difficult and hysterical they could become. Here, in their own home, caring for him in accordance with his wishes, they seemed to be at peace with his medical situation, whatever it might be. Like Gus, they even seemed to have made peace with the prospect of his death. It seemed too bad to upset the whole family when Gus would doubtless refuse any further diagnostic tests or medical treatment anyway. So I didn't mention the crackles.

The next time I visited, two or three days later, there were still more candles in the living room—and more plaster saints too. The living room seemed more than ever like a small side chapel in a Gothic cathedral. I could practically feel the guardian angels coming closer.

Gus was on his couch as usual, lying on his back, propped up with pillows. He appeared peaceful and sound asleep, but his respirations were more labored and rapid than before. There were occasional rattles of phlegm in his chest. The crackles at the base of his lungs had been replaced by coarser sounds throughout both lungs. I could hear no sounds at all at the right lung base. I assumed that the phlegm had blocked off the small tubes carrying air to that part of the lungs. I knew that a similar fate probably was shortly in store for much of the rest of the lungs unless he was vigorously treated by suctioning out the phlegm and pus.

I knew that to save his life, Gus should probably be in a hospital ICU-—with a tube in his windpipe and on a respirator to assist his breathing. He should also receive intravenous antibiotics and have a urinary catheter to monitor urine output. For Gus, that sort of intensive care would be intolerable, even if it would save his life. And he would still be left with the dead leg, the disabling stroke, and a host of other medical problems. Perhaps it was patronizing on my part, but it seemed unkind to recommend a troublesome course of action. So I simply said that his change in medical status was probably just nature taking its course, as he had wished. I said that we should concentrate on keeping him comfortable. No one dissented. Over the previous few weeks, they had all gotten used to the fact that Gus had come home to die. It was his wish, and they respected it.

A day or two later, I got a call to come quickly. Gus was dying. His breathing had stopped a couple of times but then started again. I got a death certificate from the ward office, just in case, and went quickly to the house. The living room was ablaze with the light of more candles. The room was crowded with every family member. Judith pointed proudly to her father, propped up on his pillows, eyelids closed, peaceful and in repose. Not breathing.

Gus was gone. But his corpse and his presence dominated the room.

I looked around the room. I did not see any tears. Nor were there any quiet sobs. This once difficult, loud family seemed strangely at peace with his death. They seemed proud of Gus and proud of their own role in facilitating his wishes. Gus had won his battle, and his family had helped, especially Judith and her sisters who had nursed Gus those final days. Their looks said clearly, "We're proud of Gus. Aren't you proud of Gus too? He was right, wasn't he? And wasn't he brave?"

And, by implication, they seemed to say, "You were wrong, Doctor! But never mind. You came to the house. You did what you could. But you were wrong about the amputation! Gus was right, wasn't he? Gus was a great man. We'll see him again in heaven some day, walking around on two good legs."

I saw it as a victory celebration and, partly, a victory over me and the medical profession. I had to admit that Gus had been right. He didn't have much to look forward to in this life. By departing it in the way he did—at home, cared for by his family—he had enabled them to adjust to his death and to accept it as natural. Caring for him was as beneficial to them as it was to Gus. I didn't understand all the interpersonal dynamics, but it was clear to me that Gus had made the right decision for himself and his family.

I filled out the death certificate and gave it to Judith. "The undertaker will need this," I said, and I quickly left the scene.

I never heard from that family again. But I will never forget them.

Gus taught me—once again—that patients may know better than their doctor what is best for them.

CHAPTER 15

The Atheist

—

My wife, Betty, and I once invited two couples to our home for dinner. One of the men was a lawyer and the other was a businessman. After dessert, we adjourned to the living room for an after-dinner drink. The businessman and his wife were Jewish and their son had recently had a bar mitzvah. Betty and I had attended and been impressed both by the ceremony and by the young man's poise in presiding over it. We commented about how well he had done. Our friends were proud and pleased.

Unexpectedly, the lawyer spoke up in a loud and aggressive voice: "How can any intelligent person believe that religious crap?"

I was shocked. The outburst was totally unexpected, uncomfortable, and embarrassing.

The lawyer was sure of his own convictions. He declared himself a confirmed atheist. His wife was as surprised and taken aback as the rest of us. After an awkward moment of silence, I changed the subject and conversation resumed, but raw emotions had been stirred up.

Before that evening, we had had several pleasant contacts with Bennett and Nancy, the lawyer and his wife. We had seen them at cocktail parties and home dinners. We had been to their house for dinner. We had played tennis with them. Bennett was a fine lawyer, I was sure of that, and also one of impeccable integrity. He was bright, well-read, and fun to be with. I imagined that the outburst against religious believers might have had something to do with his background. He had come from Ohio farm country to the venerable brick and ivy buildings of Harvard Yard. I wondered if Bennett had grown up in a fundamentalist Protestant church, one that was quickly discredited when he entered his new Harvard milieu. I wondered if he felt guilt or anger at deserting his own religious path, but I did not ask. And I felt that anyone with strong religious convictions would find an aggressive adversary in Bennett. I didn't want to be part of that scene in my own home again. Betty and I gradually drifted away from Bennett and Nancy, except for casual meetings at a cocktail party or a tennis club.

A few years later, a mutual friend told me that Bennett had advanced lung cancer and was a patient in Umass Hospital. I made a mental note to visit him. I made a practice of visiting friends and acquaintances when they were hospitalized, but I didn't look forward to seeing Bennett as a patient. It wasn't just the memory of his outburst about the religious beliefs of my Jewish friend; it was more that I like to bring good news, hope, and optimism. Late-stage lung cancer is not so easy to be optimistic about. The facts are often grim.

I called the patient information desk to get Bennett's room number. It was on the seventh floor. That was not good news. The seventh floor was mainly a palliative care unit. Patients there were rarely cured.

With great reluctance, I knocked on the door to his room. "Come in," replied a weak but familiar voice. I entered the room cautiously, not knowing what to expect. Although forewarned by the circumstances, I was still taken back by the appearance of my old acquaintance.

Bennett was emaciated. He had the gray pallor of one approaching death. His eyes were sunken and restless. Still, his overall body language and his manner of speech showed that a strong will to fight remained. And he seemed glad to see me and was eager to talk.

Not knowing quite how best to start the conversation, I simply said, "How is it going?"

"It's hell," he replied.

"What bothers you the most?"

It turned out that what bothered him the most at that moment was a decision that he had to make. His oncologist had urged another round of chemotherapy with a drug called interleukin. Bennett had had interleukin before. It hadn't helped. It gave him a high fever. Before that he had had other types of chemotherapy. They all had unpleasant side effects, and none had been effective. Bennett doubted that another round of interleukin would help, but he was sure that it would make him miserable. He also doubted that he had the strength to survive another round of chemotherapy. Looking at his gaunt, gray face, I doubted it too. And yet it seemed unthinkable to this strong-willed man just to give up. He felt compelled to fight, no matter how miserable it made him feel, even though in his heart he knew that fighting was futile.

"So what would you do?" He tried to shift his decision to me. But I did not want to make his decision for him. I was there as a friend, not a doctor. I had come simply to listen and to talk about whatever he wanted, not get involved with his treatment decisions. Still, he insisted on knowing what I would do if I were in his place. I tried to evade the question. I told him that I was not an oncologist and was not qualified to make a decision about chemotherapy.

Bennett would not let me evade the question: "So what would you do if you were in my place?" Finally, reluctantly, I answered him.

"I probably would not have any more chemotherapy. I don't think there is any reasonable chance that it will cure the cancer or even buy a little more time. But it will certainly cause a lot of unpleasant side effects. I would be willing to go through another course of chemotherapy, if I thought there was a good chance the chemo would help. But I wouldn't want to suffer needlessly."

I tried to lighten the mood a bit by reminding him that George Bernard Shaw once wrote, "Do not try to live forever ... you will not succeed."

Bennett smiled a bit. He liked Shaw's dry sense of humor.

Without saying it explicitly, I also left my friend with the impression that I thought it was OK not to fight his cancer any longer, that there was a time to let go and even to die when things got too bad. That dying was probably inevitable, no matter how hard he fought. When I left, he told me how much he had enjoyed our visit and that he hoped I would come back soon.

So the next day I came back. He was delighted to see me. He was in a much better mood. He had decided not to have the chemo, and he was greatly relieved by that decision. He was a proud man, used to being in charge, and somehow he felt back in control of his life, even if not much time remained.

He asked with great interest if I had seen a special TV program featuring Joseph Campbell, the mythologist, interviewed by Bill Moyers on public television the night before. The program examined the insights and power of myths, including religious myths. By chance, I had seen the program and found it interesting.

Bennett immediately began talking about myths that dealt with death and the afterlife. I was surprised that he didn't just dismiss these myths as simply primitive superstitions. From past conversations, including the one in my home a few years before, I knew that Bennett was extremely cynical about any religious beliefs. And yet here in the hospital, he was obviously intrigued with all the myths and legends—and religions—that had been built around a belief in life after death. He was particularly impressed by the fact that there were common perceptions that had been shared by many different peoples, at widely separated parts of the Earth and at many different periods of time. It seemed like a remarkable coincidence to him, or perhaps it was more than a coincidence. Perhaps it reflected some basic insight, or some basic need, held in common across many times by many people.

I don't remember saying much of anything. Mainly, I just listened. Bennett seemed to be talking as much to himself as to me. I left before long, but I promised to come back again.

A day or two later, I returned. My friend seemed quieter and more withdrawn but also more at peace. We talked a bit about the Joseph Campbell program. He was no longer a militant atheist or agnostic. Neither did he express any personal religious beliefs. He seemed content to think of death as a mystery. But regarding death as a mystery, rather than as certain annihilation, seemed to hold some comfort for him. While I listened to him recount myths dealing with death and the afterlife, I felt that Bennett was working out his own perspective.

The next day I came back to his hospital room. The bed was empty and freshly made with clean sheets. All the flowers and cards were gone. I knew what that meant. I inquired at the nursing station and was told that Bennett had died quietly a few hours before. I was not surprised, but I still felt something cold and numb and frightening in my gut. I was glad that Bennett's suffering was over, but I felt shocked by the awesome finality of the death of a friend.

A week or two later, I received a letter from Bennett's daughter, who was a third-year medical student at Yale. She told me how much my visits had meant to her father and how much it had taught her about what it means to be a real doctor. Before long, I also heard from his wife, Nancy, about how much my few visits had meant to Bennett. And finally, I heard from Bennett's son, a graduate of Harvard Medical School and a medical resident at Beth Israel Hospital in Boston. He said how much he had learned about being a physician from my conversations with his father.

I was glad that Bennett's family felt that I had been helpful, but I was also mystified as to exactly how I had helped. Frankly, I felt like a bit of a fraud. From my point of view, I had done virtually nothing. No life-saving surgery. No scientific insights. No technical know-how. I had simply paid a few courtesy visits to a dying friend, saying little and offering no conscious message. I came to visit and talk about whatever Bennett wanted to talk about. Why was that so helpful?

Looking back, I believe I know why. Having no medical message to deliver and going simply as a friend, I was there to listen. I didn't realize at the time what an enormous gift it can be to a dying patient simply to have a doctor listen intently and respond honestly and without any judgment. Through our conversations, my friend regained a sense of personal control over his medical care. He was able to say "no" to another round of chemotherapy, and he even became comfortable with the idea that it was all right to stop fighting and simply let go.

Bennett also found some emotional and maybe even spiritual comfort at the end. It didn't come from me. It came from somewhere inside him. I had no spiritual message to sell, and I was not there to preach. Instead, I simply listened sympathetically to whatever thoughts were going through his own mind, prompted by a TV program he had seen by chance. Having a doctor whom he respected listen with interest to his thoughts about the mythology surrounding death brought him comfort.

Listening with empathy can be healing.

CHAPTER 16

The Hospice Chaplain

—

Most doctors would not consider the role I played with Bennett to be their job. They would leave that role to a minister, priest, or rabbi. Hospital chaplains have had special training and experience in working with dying patients and their families. Chaplains are also more comfortable than most doctors in talking about death. One of the most effective chaplains that I have met was Sister Ann Marshall, chaplain of the Visiting Nurses Association (VNA) Hospice of central Massachusetts.

Several people I had worked with at the hospice in the late 1990s told me how effective Sister Ann was in meeting spiritual and emotional needs of the dying. I decided to see what I could learn from her.

Sister Ann was probably in her sixties when we first met. She had short, gray-white hair, eyeglasses, and a somewhat stocky build. She wore a small, white cap and a silver crucifix was pinned to her blouse. What struck me most about Sister Ann was not her appearance, but her calm and peaceful manner. She seemed totally comfortable with herself, with her life, and with death. She could give peace and comfort to the dying, I thought, because she had attained peace and comfort with death. Where did Sister Ann's inner peace come from, I wondered?

I asked Sister Ann how she became a hospice

chaplain. She told me that she came from a large family, several of whom had followed a religious calling. She had chosen to become a nun early in life. After she was already well into her religious life, an older sister in her immediate family developed an aggressive cancer that spread rapidly. The medical situation was hopeless, and her sister needed home care for terminal cancer. Sister Ann's order of nuns relieved her of other religious duties so that she could be the primary caregiver for her dying sister. She did this with great love and with a natural ability to comfort that was obvious to her superiors in the religious order.

After her sister's death, her superiors asked Sister Ann if she would like to serve other dying patients as a hospice chaplain. She agreed and completed formal training as a chaplain. Her personal knowledge of the needs of patients with life-threatening illness was deepened because of other family members who developed cancer and because she developed cancer herself. She had lived close to death for much of her life. She had also lived with a strong religious faith. She had come to peace with death.

I could understand how a devout Roman Catholic like Sister Ann could relate easily to a Catholic patient or even to a Protestant Christian. But I wondered how she could relate to a Jewish patient or a Buddhist or a Hindu or a Muslim or someone with no religious faith at all. Sister Ann told me that she always took her cues from the patient. She listened. She searched for what gave meaning to that person's life. She found that there was always something of meaning in the life of a dying patient: perhaps family, work, or a hobby. Perhaps meaning came from creating something of beauty, performing some act of kindness or generosity, or holding certain personal beliefs or religion. She talked with dying patients about those things that gave meaning to their lives. If they wished her to do so, she would pray with patients or read them inspirational passages from the Bible. But only if they wished her to do so.

She did not proselytize. She sought no deathbed conversions. Still, she was quick to rekindle old religious ties. She told me with great satisfaction of recently discussing Judaism with a dying Jewish man who had not been to temple for many years. She arranged for him to see a rabbi, who was able to reconcile the patient with his childhood beliefs, bringing a sense of peace and community that the man had not known for many years.

Sister Ann told me, "There is always something that gives meaning to a person's life. It is often quite different for different people. I search to find what brings meaning and comfort to each person I see. If I can find it, I know that it can help them get through a difficult time. It can become a source of strength when they need it most."

I thought: *Yes, that all makes sense, but that's not the whole story.* Years ago, I had read somewhere that 80 percent of interpersonal communication is nonverbal. That percentage has always seemed high to me, but I have no doubt that a lot of meaningful communication is nonverbal. As I looked at Sister Ann sitting there so relaxed, her body language radiated peace. It seemed to me that an important part of her ministry to the dying was simply sharing her own inner calm and acceptance of whatever life brings. I felt some of that calm acceptance of life settle around me while we sat there together. It felt good. I thought that if I were a hospice patient, I would look forward to a visit from Sister Ann.

In my own limited experience with dying patients, I see that most do not reach spiritual peace through spiritual counselors. More often, it comes from within the patient. However, sometimes the patient needs an empathetic listener. That role of listener can be critical. A doctor, nurse, or social worker can sometimes fill it. Often a family member or close friend can fill that role. Open-ended questions—*What helps you get through this? What are you most proud of?*—open a dialogue that prompts the patient to think through issues that might not be discussed otherwise. Sometimes no questions are needed. Simply sitting by the bedside or holding the patient's hand brings spiritual support without words.

Inner peace in the face of death can come from strong religious beliefs, as with Sister Ann, but not always, even with members of the clergy who are facing death. Inner peace can also come by thinking through one's core beliefs, as Socrates did. It brings peace of mind to get all one's affairs in order: healing relationships, saying goodbyes, making any necessary arrangements, and clearing up any pending legal or financial matters, especially a living will. Peace of mind near the end of life can also come from surprising sources, such as deathbed visions and near-death experiences.

I learned from my friend Bennett that doctors can comfort patients simply by listening to them with empathy. And by taking the time to answer a patient's questions openly and honestly. A caring discussion with a doctor can help patients retain a sense of control over their treatment. It provides a supportive environment in which patients can work out their own final beliefs regarding death. It helps bring peace of mind and acceptance.

Listening with empathy can also be done effectively by nonphysicians. The key is simply to listen with concern to whatever the patient wants to talk about.

CHAPTER 17

Letting Go

—

I woke with a start in the middle of the night. My phone was ringing, and I was on call for emergencies. I groaned. The bed was so warm and comfortable, and I hated to leave it. But the nurse's voice was urgent: *Dr. Wheeler, this is the ER. We have a ruptured aneurysm coming by ambulance from Hubbard Hospital. How soon can you get here?*

A ruptured abdominal aortic aneurysm, or AAA, is a life-threatening emergency. The abdominal portion of the aorta is nearly the diameter of a garden hose. It carries blood under high pressure, enough to perfuse the lower half of the body. If the wall of the abdominal aorta becomes weakened by disease, the wall stretches and the vessel swells. The more it swells, the weaker it gets. The weaker it gets, the more it swells. This vicious cycle goes on until finally the aorta ruptures. A free rupture of the aorta into the abdominal cavity can be fatal within a few seconds. So the diagnosis of a ruptured AAA usually leads to a dash to the operating room. Speed is critical, often life saving.

On this night, our ER had been called by Hubbard Regional Hospital, a community hospital that refers complicated and difficult patients to our medical center about 20 miles away. They had requested emergency helicopter transport because the patient, a 75-year-old man, was in shock. However, stormy weather had grounded our helicopter. I was told that the patient was on his way by ambulance, but he was not expected for half an hour. That gave me time to get to the ER before the patient arrived. The patient's only hope was for us to stop the bleeding rapidly, transfuse blood to restore normal blood volume, and replace the diseased aorta with a plastic graft. I had anesthesiologists and nurses called in from home to set up the operating room (OR).

When the ambulance arrived, the patient was accompanied by the referring doctor and a nurse from Hubbard Regional Hospital. Normally, the ambulance crew was a driver and an emergency medical technician; I couldn't recall both a referring doctor and nurse coming along with a patient. The reason was quickly explained: The patient was the nurse's father. Being well aware of the life-and-death crisis, she wanted to be with him. The doctor worked closely with the nurse and wanted to support her. He also wanted to explain the patient's complicated medical history.

The patient was pale and sweating and only feebly responsive. No blood pressure was obtainable. There was a tender, pulsating mass about ten cm wide in the abdomen.

I told Paul Burke, the vascular surgical fellow who would assist me with the surgery, to take the patient straight to the OR and prepare him for surgery. I stayed behind to talk briefly to the daughter and the referring doctor to learn more about the patient's medical history.

The conversation went something like this: I asked, "Except for the aneurysm, is he in good health?"

The doctor replied, "No. He's on kidney dialysis three times a week. He hates it. That is why he refused surgery for the aneurysm six months ago when it was first detected."

"Why is he on dialysis?"

"He has multiple myeloma (a type of cancer) and it has destroyed his kidneys."

"What is his life expectancy with the myeloma?"

"The oncologist says about three to six months."

"What's his quality of life?"

"Not great. He hates dialysis, and he has a lot of bone pain from the myeloma. He doesn't eat well, and he is losing weight. He also requires transfusions for anemia from time to time."

I could hardly believe this litany of medical problems. As one problem after another was added to the list, it seemed virtually impossible to think that any elderly patient with so many medical problems could survive surgery for a ruptured aneurysm with shock. I also was impressed that he had previously refused surgery when he was in much better shape, presumably because of the cancer and his deteriorating quality of life. I became less and less interested in surgical heroics, even though we had called in the OR team and were all set to operate.

"Let's think this through," I said to the daughter. "If we operate, there's a very good chance he will not survive the surgery. Even if he does survive, he will certainly be in for a rocky course in the ICU. He will undoubtedly be on a respirator for a long time, not to mention dialysis. With his resistance lowered, he will be a prime candidate for infection and multi-organ failure. It is extremely unlikely that he could survive and leave the

ICU, but he might well have a long ICU stay that would be quite distressing to him and his loved ones. If by some miracle he survives the post-op period, he will die of his cancer in a few months anyway. Do you think that if he understood all this, he would want us to operate? He refused surgery when he was in much better shape."

"What's the alternative?" the doctor asked.

"If we don't operate," I said, "he will probably die quietly in the next few hours. But he will never have to go through a long ICU stay on life support machines or suffer through a progressive downhill course and death from cancer."

The doctor said nothing. Neither did the daughter.

By this time the patient's wife had arrived. She was listening intently. The daughter turned to her mother and said, "What do you think Dad would want?"

"You know what he would want."

"He wouldn't want the surgery."

"No, he wouldn't."

I said, "Let's see if we can ask him what he wants. If he's able to understand, we need to get his permission to operate." So I went up to the pre-operative holding area just outside the main OR, an area where pre-anesthetic drugs are administered and final preparations are made prior to surgery. The patient's eyes were closed. He barely opened them when I spoke to him. He seemed far away, curiously detached from his surroundings and his life-threatening situation. Still, he seemed to understand what I was saying.

Softly, gently, I tried to explain his situation as honestly as I could. I told him that the outlook was not good, with or without surgery. I said that he might die very soon without surgery, but that his long-term outlook wasn't very good, either, even if the surgery was successful. Given his overall medical condition, I said that declining surgery was an understandable option and that he had the right to decide for himself. Then I asked if he wanted us to do the surgery. Faintly but quite definitely, he shook his head "no." I felt that he understood the situation and that he was expressing his true wishes. I also thought that under the same circumstances I would make the same decision.

I told the OR team that I was canceling the planned surgery. I apologized for calling them in from home and disturbing their night's sleep. Some looked relieved to go home sooner than they had expected, but others looked disgruntled that their night's sleep had been interrupted unnecessarily. I said once again that I was sorry to disturb their sleep, but I had called them into the hospital in order to speed up life-saving surgery.

We transferred the patient from the OR suite to a quiet, private room. I had the bright room lights dimmed. A blood transfusion had been started in the OR and was still running. I slowed down the rate but kept the transfusion dripping steadily. I realized the transfusion was futile, but I felt that it might somehow be comforting to his wife and daughter. A token of treatment that said he was not abandoned. Orders were left for the nurses to check from time to time, primarily to see if the patient was comfortable and to see if they could help the family in any way. I stayed until I was sure the family was comfortably settled, satisfied simply to sit near him in a quiet, darkened room.

Then I drove home and went to sleep promptly.

On bedside rounds the next morning I was told that the patient had died quietly in the night and that the wife and daughter had said they were grateful for his care. So ended another night when I was on call for vascular emergencies. I didn't think of that patient again for several months. What brought him to mind once more was a conversation with Paul Burke, the vascular surgery fellow who assisted me that night in getting ready for an emergency operation that never happened.

Paul knew that I was wrestling with the decision of when to retire from the practice of surgery. As chief of surgery at three different hospitals over 35 years, I had seen too many older surgeons, once highly regarded for their clinical judgment and their technical skill, continue operating far too long. Their surgical skills had failed to advance with changes in the field. I knew too that it is hard to judge yourself. There is a tendency to think that your years of experience outweigh any failure to stay up-to-date with the newest procedures or to slow down with age. I wanted to go out playing at the top of my game— and not have to be prompted by some embarrassed younger colleague. In short, I had nearly decided to stop operating. Paul knew this.

"I hope you won't retire, Dr. Wheeler," I was surprised to hear him say this one day, as he neared the end of his fellowship. "It would be a real loss to other vascular fellows."

I felt flattered but surprised and, frankly, dubious. Because my younger colleagues were doing more surgery than I was, I assumed they were correspondingly slicker and quicker in the OR and more up-to-date on the latest techniques. I said so to Paul.

"Yes, but you have something to teach that the others don't have," he said. "I learned more from one of your patients than from any other patient all year. I doubt that you would ever guess which patient it was."

I had to admit that no patient popped into my mind as the most instructive teaching case of his entire fellowship year. Paul then reminded me of the ruptured aneurysm patient of months ago. I had practically forgotten that night. The diagnosis was obvious. The decision not to operate seemed equally obvious. No operation had been done. How valuable a learning experience could that have been?

Paul told me that after I had gone home to bed that night, he had stayed in the hospital to follow the patient's course. The wife and daughter sat on either side of the patient's bed, each holding one of his hands. All seemed peaceful in the darkened room. For two or three hours, not much happened. Then the patient opened his eyes slightly and seemed to be more alert. Some soft but apparently meaningful words were exchanged, after which the patient closed his eyes and seemed to be resting peacefully. His breathing became slow and shallow. After a while, his breathing stopped for several seconds, then started again. Again it stopped. And this time failed to start again. His wife and daughter said nothing. They held his hands for a few more minutes and then quietly left the room. Paul pronounced the patient dead and filled out the death certificate. It was all very peaceful.

I wondered what the lessons had been that had made such an impression on Paul. The patient's death was expected and peaceful. The family seemed peaceful too. Their vigil had been an effective balm for their troubled emotions. Slowly, I realized that that was just the point.

I felt honor bound to act as the patient wished. By that point in my career, it seemed unthinkable not to honor his wish—even knowing it was a death sentence. Earlier in my career, when I was Paul's age, I would probably not have had the experience or the courage to allow a patient to die without putting him through a heroic but futile operation.

"I know how he might have died, Dr. Wheeler. I have seen too many patients die that way in our ICU."

I looked at Paul's face. It showed the sadness of seeing too many patients die badly. I knew that sadness. I had felt it too. I had seen many more bad deaths than Paul. Perhaps that is why I was so reluctant to rush this patient to surgery. I knew that although we might pro-long his life slightly, there was a near-certainty that he would die in a few days despite heroic life-support mea-sures. And there was also the moral and legal issue of the patient's consent. He knew the stakes and had refused surgery. I knew that under the emotional pressure of the crisis, I could have pushed the family into opting for surgery—a near certainty of setting the stage for a bad death with painful memories for the family. Paul felt that he had learned something about preventing a bad death and supporting the family—the most important lesson that he had learned that year.

I remembered that a wise and famous man had faced a similar decision about emergency surgery for a ruptured aneurysm. He was 79 years old, and he refused the operation even though he had no overwhelming medical problems. There was no question about his men-tal competency. He was the most famous scientist of the

20th century. His name was Albert Einstein.

On Friday, April 15, 1955, Einstein entered the Princeton Infirmary with severe pain from an abdominal aortic aneurysm. A prominent vascular surgeon from New York urged emergency surgery, but Einstein refused. His condition stabilized and even improved so that on Sunday he asked for his notepad so he could continue work. However, shortly after midnight, the aneurysm burst, and he died immediately.

I don't know why Einstein refused surgery. Perhaps it was because aortic surgery was relatively new in the mid-1950s. More likely, it seems to me, he simply felt that his life was drawing to its close and perhaps a ruptured aneurysm was a quicker and better way to die than some others. One month earlier, following the death of a longtime friend, he had written: "Now he has preceded me briefly in bidding farewell to this strange world. This signifies nothing. For us believing physicists, the distinction between past, present, and future is only an illusion, even if a stubborn one."

Was Einstein wise to refuse surgery? I don't know, but I do know that it was his decision to make. And I have known many other patients who decided otherwise and who suffered through a long and painful postoperative course, only to die anyway.

CHAPTER 18

The Surgeon-in-Chief

—

Francis D. Moore, a larger-than-life figure with many talents, rose rapidly to national prominence in surgery. At age 35, he was appointed Moseley professor of surgery at Harvard Medical School and surgeon in chief at the Peter Bent Brigham Hospital, one of the most prestigious positions in American surgery. He made major contributions to the postoperative care of surgical patients, particularly in the management of intravenous fluids, electrolytes, and nutrition. These advances led to fewer complications and lower rates of mortality following major surgery. He also supervised research leading to successful transplantation of the kidney and the liver. Perhaps more than anyone else, he brought laboratory science to the practice of surgery. His portrait was on the cover of *Time* magazine in 1963, and he was held up as the foremost example of a new breed of surgeons who used scientific methods to expand and improve surgical care.

Medical students were in awe of him, myself included. We looked forward to his lectures. He was a powerful speaker with a resonant, slightly raspy baritone voice that dominated any auditorium. And he had a natural theatrical presence that commanded attention, much as a great actor can command attention merely by his presence on stage. It was said that he had even considered a career in the theater while a student at Harvard College. He was a prominent member of the Hasty Pudding Club, the Harvard student theater group.

Francis D. Moore, MD, the Surgeon-In-Chief: He was my surgical mentor and career guide. He offered me a position in his department. Credit: Time Magazine (May 3, 1963)

I first met Dr. Moore when I was starting my second year in medical school. In a summer job at Meharry Medical College in Nashville, I had worked with Dr. Paul Hahn on the experimental use of radioactive isotopes in the treatment of cancer. When I returned to medical school in the fall, I wanted to continue this work. I developed a research protocol to treat tumors in inbred strains of mice. If the results were promising in animals, I wanted to treat patients under the supervision of a cancer specialist. To get started, I needed a faculty sponsor who could provide me with access to laboratory facilities, radioisotope instruments, and discretionary funding. Any sponsor would need to make a giant leap of faith.

I was only 20 years old, had little research experience, and little time to devote to the project, given the demands of medical school. Not surprisingly, every faculty member I asked to sponsor my research turned me down. Finally, after several rejections, someone suggested that I speak to Dr. Moore.

So, one day I found myself face to face with the Great Man. He had a strong body, about six feet tall and 200 pounds, and moved with great energy. His brown hair was cut close to his head, almost military in style. His eyes stared steadily at me. I found his direct gaze intimidating. I felt that I was being weighed and measured by those eyes. I also felt that I had very little time to make my case to this busy and important man. However, he listened quite intently to what I had to say. When I was done, to my surprise, he said to speak to Ms. Peggy Ball, the director of his research laboratory, and to tell her that he said to make a place for me. His quick decision changed my whole life.

My research in Dr. Moore's lab got off to a slow start, but ultimately things went well. Based on promising results in experimental animals, by my senior year in medical school, cancer patients at the Peter Bent Brigham Hospital were treated with radioactive colloidal gold. Dr. Moore arranged for me to present my research to a prestigious national surgical society while I was still a medical student. When I finished medical school, he persuaded me to choose a career in surgery; and he gave me a position in his surgical training program. When I finished the training program, he gave me a position on his faculty. Because of his mentoring, I became an academic surgeon.

I will always be grateful for the opportunities he

provided me. He was my professional father figure. However, like many father-son relationships, our relationship got a bit rocky when I began to grow up professionally. I disagreed with some of his plans for me and insisted on going my own way. He must have felt that I was an ungrateful and disobedient child, and I felt that he was an overbearing and dictatorial boss. Fortunately, time resolved those issues, and we regained a warm relationship.

After he retired from surgery, "Frannie" Moore made significant contributions to health-care planning, biostatistics, and societal and philosophic issues in health care. I admired his motivation to continue after retirement to contribute to society in different ways, and I admired his impressive ability to do so. In his later years, I would still see him at national meetings. In the Q&A session after a presentation, he would often limp to a floor microphone and identify himself in that resonant baritone: Francis Moore, Boston. The announcement was quite superfluous; everyone in the audience knew that he was Francis Moore from Boston. His comments or questions were always cogent and insightful. I was impressed with his intellect, as always, but I sometimes wondered why he needed to take the microphone quite so often.

As the years went by, he began to decline physically, though his mind stayed sharp. He began to walk with a limp, and I suspected that he had degenerative arthritis in his hips or knees. Also, I heard that he had borderline heart failure and was on multiple medications for cardiac problems.

He moved into Fox Hill, an upscale assisted-living facility that attracted many physician retirees. Although it was quite attractive, even elegant by most standards, I found Fox Hill depressing. The residents included many who used wheelchairs or walkers. Many were seriously limited, physically or mentally. I thought that it would be hard to live there and not be constantly reminded that physical decay, major disability, and death were not too far down the road for most residents. I wondered if Frannie, who had always seemed so strong and capable and in charge of his life, didn't find it depressing to live in that environment. But I never asked him that question.

One visit was particularly depressing to me, and it certainly must have been to him as well. We were walking down a hallway in Fox Hill and saw a large, white-haired man in his seventies slumped to one side of his chair, eyes closed, mouth open, and face paralyzed on one side from an old stroke.

"Why, it's John Brooks! John, look who's come to see us. It's Brownie. You remember Brownie. ... Brownie Wheeler. Say hello to Brownie, John."

John Brooks slowly opened his eyes, looked at Dr. Moore and, after a moment, gave a glance at me and then looked back at Dr. Moore. He said nothing. I was not sure that he recognized Dr. Moore, and I was sure that he did not recognize me. He also seemed far beyond caring whether he had any visitors.

What was particularly sad was that John Brooks had been one of Dr. Moore's first chief residents. After finishing the residency, he stayed on the surgical faculty, and over the years he became one of Dr. Moore's strongest supporters and closest friends. He was a tall man, perhaps six feet three inches, with a large, strong body. I was always a bit in awe of this sturdy and imposing senior surgeon. To see him out of touch with his surroundings, partially paralyzed, unable to recognize even close friends and associates, was painful to me. I couldn't begin to guess how much more painful it must have been for Dr. Moore, with whom he had been so close for so long.

Dr. Moore had invited me to come to Fox Hill that day to look at some valuable medical books. He was downsizing his possessions and disposing of many objects he had acquired over his long career. One book was of great historical interest: a textbook of anatomy, published in 1543 and written by Andreas Vesalius, professor of surgery at the University of Padua, Italy. Johann von Calcar, a protégé of the Renaissance painter Titian, had illustrated it. With illustrations that are the pinnacle of anatomic art, the book is widely regarded as the foundation of modern medicine. It established the importance of precise observations and thoughtful analysis of those observations in order to understand the functioning of the body. Of the 300 original copies, many were lost or damaged over the centuries. After a long search, Dr. Moore had found and purchased an original copy with all its pages intact. Now he wanted to find a suitable home where it would be honored and appropriately cared for. He thought first of Harvard, but Harvard already had three copies. He thought next of the Armed Forces National Medical School, where he had consulted extensively, but he was concerned about government proposals to close the school. Finally, he thought of the University of Massachusetts Medical School, which had a rare books library and a respected Department of Surgery. He called me up and said that he would like to donate his rare copy of the historic Vesalius volume to UMass Medical School in my honor. I was floored. And thrilled. And grateful.

Along with the Vesalius, he also donated a later edition (about 1610) of one of the first textbooks of surgery. Written by the famous French surgeon Ambrose Paré in the 1590s, it is generally regarded as the foundation of modern surgery, based on careful observation of clinical results and honest reporting of what went wrong, as well as what went right. To a surgeon, the Paré textbook is perhaps more interesting than the Vesalius, even if the illustrations are not as beautiful. I was thrilled to have Dr. Moore give our library both books.

Donation of Rare Books to Univeristy of Massachusetts Medical School: Andreas Vesalius, 1543; Ambrose Paré, 1610 (From left: Dr. Francis Moore, Donor; Dr. Aaron Lazare, Recipient; Dr. H. Brownell Wheeler, Honoree)

There was an impressive ceremony at UMass Medical School in which Dr. Moore formally presented the rare historical volumes to the school. Dr. Moore had primed me ahead of time about educating the audience as to the history and the importance of these rare books. I worked diligently for weeks on the presentation. I made special slides to show and carefully rehearsed my talk. When the time approached for my presentation, Dr. Moore stood up, glanced at some notes he had scribbled on an envelope, and gave a talk covering my presentation.

I didn't mind Dr. Moore taking the time designated for me to give the talk that he had told me to prepare. It was his day, a day that his own generosity had made possible.

The book gifts were so unexpected, so generous, that I felt more warmly toward him than ever. So a couple of years later, I was shocked when I learned that my professional father figure, a man I regarded as larger than life, perhaps the most talented individual I had ever known, had put a pistol to his head and pulled the trigger. One of the greatest careers in American surgery ended with the crack of a gunshot.

"Why did he do it?"

I kept asking myself that question. It was hard to believe that the man I had respected so much would kill himself. He must have had good reasons, I thought. But his sudden, unexpected, and violent death must have been a terrible shock to his family. His wife was in the apartment when he fired the shot. I hope that the housekeeper kept her out of the den where he died. That scene must have been horrendous. I still refuse to let myself imagine what it was like.

I rationalized that he must have thought he was sparing his family the pain of some long illness or profound disability that he saw as inevitable. Or perhaps, I thought, he was profoundly depressed. So deeply despondent that he was no longer the rational, self-controlled man I had always admired. Still, it was a premeditated act. His son told me that Dr. Moore had bought the gun many years ago. Several months before the suicide, the son had asked what had happened to the pistol.

"Oh, I got rid of that years ago." But it wasn't true. Frannie Moore still had the pistol hidden away. It is hard to escape the conclusion that he had realized a time might come when he would want to end his life, even against the wishes of his family, and he had retained the means to do so. The gun was his ticket out of an increasingly unhappy life.

He was 87. He had recently been hospitalized for cardiac problems, and he was taking several medications without much improvement in his chronic fatigue and shortness of breath. The prospects for returning to vigorous good health were quite unlikely. As far as I know, his mind remained sharp to the end; but to him, it may have been apparent that his brain too was aging. For someone with such a remarkable career, loss of mental capability would seem an especially cruel burden to bear.

I will never know his exact motivations; but I can't condemn my old chief, much as I regret the way he chose to end his life.

CHAPTER 19

Young Surgeons and Suicide

—

The suicide of Dr. Francis Moore was tragic, but he had had a long and remarkable career. His early promise had been fulfilled. But I have also known gifted young surgeons who ended their lives by suicide. Their career potential was never realized.

In the mid-1960s, Dan P was a senior resident in surgery. He was a good-looking man with a square jaw, light brown hair, and large glasses with clear plastic rims. He had a lovely wife and four young children. I had gotten to know Dan well when I supervised his residency training at the West Roxbury VA Hospital.

One evening we were chatting in the residents' office when Dan told me that he had been rereading his father's diary. His father had shot and killed himself some years before. Dan said he was trying to find out what had been going through his father's mind before his suicide. Dan seemed so matter-of-fact and emotionally detached from his father's death that it seemed a perfectly reasonable thing for him to read the diary. Later, it seemed an obvious clue that I should have pursued.

Another clue brought Dan's precarious state of mind to my attention in a startling way. I had assigned him to do a routine surgical procedure under the supervision of Dr. Richard Warren. The purpose of the operation was to remove a fibrous white chain of sympathetic nerves that control blood flow and sweating in the leg. The procedure can improve skin blood flow in patients with poor circulation. Dr. Warren had helped to popularize the procedure and was a recognized expert in this type of surgery. It was not technically difficult and should have been well within the capabilities of a senior resident like Dan, especially under expert supervision. Or so I thought.

All tissue removed at surgery goes to pathology. The pathologist examines the tissue and verifies the diagnosis. It is a hospital rule that often seemed unnecessary to me, but this operation changed my mind. Dan had carried out the scheduled procedure, apparently uneventfully, and the patient had been returned to the recovery room. About an hour later, I received an urgent phone call from the chief of pathology. I was needed immediately in the pathology laboratory to examine the tissue Dan removed. I couldn't imagine what could make my presence in the path lab needed so urgently. When I got there, it was immediately apparent that there was a serious problem. The bald-headed, red-faced, bespectacled chief of pathology, Dr. Ira Gore, was sitting at a microscope with a shocked and sober expression on his face. He offered no friendly greeting or small talk.

"Look at this slide."

I looked in the microscope and saw what looked, under magnification, like a cross-section of a garden hose. Under the circumstances, it could only be the ureter, the tube that carries urine from the kidney to the bladder. I was shocked. There was no way that the ureter should have been removed in this operation. How could this have happened?

"Your resident says this is the lumbar sympathetic chain that you told him to remove."

For a moment, I was speechless. Then I thanked Dr. Gore for notifying me so promptly and said that I would deal with the situation.

I went back to my office and paged Dan to come to my office at once. He arrived shortly, looking totally unperturbed.

"How did your operation go this morning?"

"Very well," he replied. "It went just like in Dr. Warren's book." And he went on, in response to my questions, to describe what he had done in some detail, including how he had identified the sympathetic chain of nerves by its location and the presence of periodic nodules, called ganglia. It all sounded perfect. Too perfect. It was word for word the description in Dr. Warren's *Atlas of Surgical Procedures*. And such a picture-perfect operation had obviously never happened in this patient. But, equally obviously, Dan believed it had.

I told Dan not to leave the hospital and that I would be back in touch with him before long. Then I searched out Dr. George Gifford, the junior resident assigned to the operation. It turned out he had never seen an operation like this before. He had recognized that there was some discrepancy between what he had expected from his reading about the operation and what he saw Dan doing. But he didn't challenge Dan because of Dan's seniority and Dan's complete assurance as to what he was doing.

All of which raised the question, where was Dr. Warren? He would have known in a split-second if Dan mistook the ureter for the sympathetic chain. With some trepidation, I called Dr. Warren and told him what had happened. Gingerly, I asked what he saw during the operation. It turned out that Dr. Warren had not scrubbed in on the procedure. He had remained in the surgeon's lounge, talking with the other surgeons and drinking coffee. Several times he had stepped into the operating room and asked how the procedure was going. He had asked if Dan was ready for him to scrub in and join the surgical team. Each time, Dan had said everything was going beautifully and that Dr. Warren wasn't needed. So he never scrubbed in.

Dr. Warren was obviously shocked by what had happened. He took full responsibility for the outcome, and he said that he would handle all communication with the patient and his family. He ordered an X-ray that showed the ureter had been clipped off just below the left kidney and was missing from that point until just above the bladder. It also showed a normally functioning right kidney. After consultation with Dr. Herb Talbot, the chief of urology, Dr. Warren and Dr. Talbot decided to remove the kidney that had been blocked by removal of its ureter. The other kidney showed normal function by X-ray studies, and a patient with only one kidney has the same life expectancy as a patient with two kidneys. Some people are born with only one kidney and never know it.

Dr. Warren and Dr. Talbot agreed that the safest, surest way to avoid further risks and complications for the patient was to remove the blocked kidney. At the time the kidney was removed, Dr. Warren also did the procedure originally booked.

The patient had an uneventful convalescence. The circulation to his leg was better, with his foot noticeably warmer and redder than before. He and his family seemed well pleased with the outcome. As far as I know, there were no long-term complications.

It seemed to the entire surgical staff that no fully rational surgeon could mistake a ureter for a chain of sympathetic nerves. Was Dan hallucinating, we wondered? Could he operate safely on other patients? Dan was put on a leave of absence and underwent psychiatric evaluation.

Some months later, he was allowed to return to the Brigham hospital residency. After a few weeks back in the training program, one evening he went out into the backyard and shot himself in the head with his father's revolver. It was an exact replay of his father's suicide, just as he had described it to me months before.

I believe that Dan was a gifted person with a severe, but unrecognized mental illness, most likely manic-depressive disorder. In the manic phase, he could imagine that his surgical procedures were carried out perfectly. In the depressive phase, he could believe that his suffering could only be ended by suicide. His death was a great tragedy for his wife and four young children. But I felt that Dan could not tell right from wrong with respect to suicide any more than he could tell the ureter from the sympathetic chain in the operating room. Dan was able to see only what his illness allowed him to see.

Some years later, at UMass Medical School, another of my surgical residents committed suicide. She was a bright young woman, full of promise, and her death was a severe blow to me and to everyone else in our department. Her name was Mary M.

A first-year resident just starting her surgical

training, Mary was a graduate of Harvard College and Boston University Medical School. A slender woman with the lean body of a runner, she had been a standout athlete at Harvard. On first meeting, she seemed a bit tense but no more than many high achievers. Her academic record was excellent. We expected great things from Mary.

In the first few months of her residency, it became apparent that all was not well with her. She seemed listless and unhappy. She hardly ever smiled. Someone in her confidence learned that she was severely depressed and had even considered suicide. After a psychiatric consultation, she was voluntarily hospitalized on the psychiatric ward at Worcester Memorial Hospital. A few days later, I went to see Mary. She told me that she was feeling much better.

Mary told me that she had never wanted to be a surgeon. Her father was a surgeon, and she had wanted to please him by following in his footsteps. She knew how much it meant to him, but her heart was not in a surgical career. She said that her depression dated back several years. She reassured me that her depression had nothing to do with our surgical training program. In fact, she said, her fellow residents and the surgical staff had all been quite supportive and helpful.

I told her that there were many possible careers in medicine and that I was sure we could help her find a career more suitable for her. I asked her to come to my office for a long chat about future career opportunities after she was discharged from the hospital and she felt like talking more. In the meantime, I tried to find some nonstressful medical role for her to fill out the remainder of the year. I spoke to Dr. Guido Majno, our empathetic, warm-hearted chair of pathology, about Mary spending the rest of the year doing research under his supervision. He agreed, subject to the Department of Surgery paying her salary and expenses, and I asked Mary to see me and discuss these arrangements.

Two days before Valentine's Day, I sat down with Mary to discuss plans for the year. She was quiet but calm. She seemed at peace with herself. She agreed to do research for the rest of the year in the pathology department, and she thanked me for working out the arrangements. I told her that, quite honestly, I hadn't fully worked out all the details, especially the finances. But I was optimistic that we could find the funds to continue her salary.

As we sat there, I thought that she seemed strangely unconcerned about the salary. Looking back later, her indifference to her salary was an obvious clue to her state of mind. Why worry about your salary when you have decided to kill yourself in two days? Sadly, I wasn't sharp enough to pick up on that obvious clue. I have blamed myself a hundred times since for not being more perceptive. Perhaps I could have prevented the tragedy about to unfold.

Leaving my office, Mary thanked me once again for talking to Dr. Majno on her behalf. And she stressed again that her depression had been present for years and was totally unrelated to her experiences in our surgical training program. I did not realize that she was saying goodbye and trying to assuage the guilt I would feel later.

Two days later, on Valentine's Day, Mary was expected at her family's home in Cambridge for dinner.

She did not show up. They called her apartment. There was no answer. As the hours went by, the family became increasingly apprehensive. Finally, her father drove out to her apartment. He found his daughter hanging from the shower rod in the bathroom. She had been dead for hours.

I could not imagine any greater trauma for a father.

Word of Mary's death spread quickly. Within hours, unannounced, the chief of psychiatry, Dr. Aaron Lazare, appeared in my office. He told me Mary's suicide would traumatize our whole department. He offered to obtain an anonymous psychiatric consultation for any of our resident staff members who wished to receive it. He offered to bring out a female psychiatrist from Boston to see our female residents. He suggested that we have open meetings where the residents and staff could vent their pent-up emotions. I arranged such a meeting, and about 50 people attended. I had trouble keeping the tone of the meeting constructive. People felt angry. People felt guilty. They blamed themselves. They blamed the program. They blamed the faculty. They blamed me.

I offered to provide anonymous psychiatric consultation, paid for by the Department of Surgery. I told them that anyone who wished a free consultation should contact Dr. Lazare's secretary, who would arrange a confidential appointment. Later, Dr. Lazare told me that many of our residents chose to be seen by a psychiatrist, including every female resident.

I attended the memorial mass, along with several of our faculty and many residents. The small church was packed. Perhaps it was my imagination, but the priest seemed quite uncomfortable in his role. He wanted to say good things about Mary. He wanted somehow to bring comfort to the family. But her suicide was abhorrent to him and probably a mortal sin in his mind. As I recall, he said that Mary could not go directly to heaven since she had committed suicide. Neither was she condemned to hell, he emphasized. Instead, her spirit was in some intermediate realm, with the real possibility that God, in his infinite love and compassion, might yet redeem her.

The priest's words did not bring much comfort to me, but I hoped they brought some comfort to Mary's family and friends. I was glad that the priest offered some hope of eternal redemption by a loving God. From my perspective, no God worthy of the name would condemn Mary. She was a good and decent person, but she was trapped in a black depression, able to see only one way out.

Sitting there in her memorial service, I wondered if that same scenario of hopeless depression wasn't also responsible for the deaths of many other suicide victims, especially Dr. Francis Moore, my old chief. I remembered his portrait on the cover of Time magazine, looking resolute and invincible. I felt sad for them all, and especially sad for the loved ones they left behind in such a painful way. But I couldn't blame them. I could not see the world though their eyes, so how could I judge them?

Dan and Mary were sensitive, caring, and thoughtful. I cannot believe that they wanted to inflict pain on their families. Or that they deliberately threw away a promising career of service to others. Instead, I believe they were mired in a deep depression that overwhelmed their better natures. Surgical training is rigorous and exhausting. It is hard on a tender or damaged psyche.

As the director of surgical training programs, I learned painfully the importance of being alert to signs of mental illness and getting help early.

CHAPTER 20

Death With a Doctor's Help

—

I still hate to think of the violent deaths of Dr. Francis Moore, Dan and Mary. Or of other violent suicides—those who jumped off bridges or out of tall buildings, or drove a car into a concrete bridge abutment at 100 miles an hour. It's no wonder that many people who want to commit suicide would like a doctor's help in finding an easier and more peaceful way to end their lives.

Some physicians have been willing to write recurring prescriptions for barbiturate sleeping pills that a patient can hoard until they have built up a lethal cache. Those physicians usually play this role behind the scenes and only for highly selected patients who are suffering from some painful, incurable disease. Ending their pain, rather than prolonging their suffering, seems a kindness, even at the expense of what little remains of their life. The public in many states is sympathetic to this view. A referendum that legalizes physician-assisted suicide has been passed in four states, as of this writing, and narrowly defeated elsewhere.

Oregon was the first state to legalize physician-assisted suicide. I once had the opportunity to have a leisurely lunch with the physician who assisted the first patient to die under the new law in Oregon. He was also involved in subsequent suicides. I was interested to learn about the Oregon experience.

Our meeting took place in Amsterdam in 2001. I had been invited to speak at an international conference on end-of-life care. A physician from Oregon was also an invited speaker. She had played a major role in promoting the citizens' referendum that legalized physician-assisted suicide in Oregon. She was a pleasant, attractive, and friendly woman, about 40 years old. After we had given our talks one morning, she invited me to join her and her husband for lunch. He was also a physician, just as friendly and pleasant as she and about the same age. I was intrigued that he had significant personal experience with physician-assisted suicide and had been the first to assist under the new law.

As it turned out, my new acquaintance had had no intention or desire to be the first physician to assist a suicide under the new legal framework in Oregon. In fact, he was surprised and appalled when he was suddenly placed in a national spotlight. His story was simple. He had had an older woman patient who requested his help under the new law, and he had had no doubts that the request was appropriate. She had adult children who supported her request and pleaded with him to relieve her suffering, even if the only way to do so was assisting her suicide. It was hard not to sympathize with their wishes. After some soul-searching, he became convinced that she was just the sort of patient that the voters of Oregon had in mind when they voted to legalize physician-assisted suicide. He had no idea that she would be the first patient to die under the new law.

The logistics went smoothly. After appropriate notifications, and at a time set by the patient and her family, she swallowed a medication to prevent nausea and vomiting, followed by a lethal dose of barbiturates. With her family and the physician at the bedside, she went rapidly into a deeper and deeper sleep until she finally stopped breathing. It was quick—about half an hour. It was peaceful. It was a relief to the family. It was deeply moving, even awesome, but somewhat unsettling to the physician. However he justified it, there was no question that he had facilitated the death of another human being. It was an unsettling feeling, more so than he had expected.

The death was reported by the physician to the authorities. Soon, it became known that this patient had been the first person to die in Oregon as a result of the new law. To the physician's dismay, he was besieged by phone calls from the local and national media. He found himself being interviewed on National Public Radio and national TV shows. *What does it feel like to kill someone, Doctor?* It was not the sort of question any physician would like to hear. Still, most of the interviewers were sympathetic.

Our conversation in Amsterdam took place a few years after that first death under the Oregon law. The doctor said he had no second thoughts about its justification, but he still felt uncomfortable about the fact that his own actions had caused the death of another person. He found it hard to shake an illogical sense of guilt, despite the grateful Christmas cards he continued to receive from the patient's children each year. Furthermore, as he provided lethal prescriptions later for other patients, he continued to feel uncomfortable about what he was doing.

Finally, he asked a patient who had sought his

help in ending his life if he would consider an alternative course: fasting and restriction of fluids. He promised to remain in close touch and minimize pain or any symptoms due to dehydration. The patient agreed. Fasting proved to be no problem since the disease process had destroyed his appetite. Fluid restriction led to an uncomfortably dry mouth and throat, but this was helped greatly by glycerin swabs and ice chips. After two or three days, the patient was sleeping most of the time. After five or six days, he was sometimes hard to arouse. After a week, a deep sleep gradually became a coma. Later, the patient's breathing became irregular and, a day or two later, finally stopped altogether. The doctor was relieved that it had been so easy. And that he felt comfortable about his role. He resolved to make fasting his first recommendation to patients with terminal disease who wanted to avoid a prolonged and painful death. As of the time I talked to him, he had had similar outcomes with other terminally ill patients. He seemed surprised that the patients usually died within a few days, despite the fact that they were all nearing death from their underlying disease anyway.

He pointed out that one of the drawbacks of physician-assisted suicide is that many sick and elderly patients find it difficult to swallow all the pills required. They would much prefer to have a lethal injection by the doctor. But that would be illegal. The Oregon law allows the doctor to write a lethal prescription and the pharmacist to fill it, but the patient must swallow the drug. A lethal injection would be against the law. It would amount to euthanasia. There are only a few places in the world where euthanasia is legal: the Netherlands, Luxembourg, Albania, and Belgium.

By chance, our family learned something about euthanasia in the Netherlands through personal experience. About 20 years ago, our youngest daughter married a Dutchman. They had met at Cornell University, where they were both graduate students: Mary was studying French literature; Rogier was studying business. Their wedding was in our church, and the reception was in our backyard.

Several of Rogier's relatives flew across the Atlantic to be present, among them his maternal grandmother. She was a model of European elegance and sophistication. Of medium height and trim build, she had white hair brushed back in a stylish wave. Her clothes were tailored in discrete but striking continental style. Her English was excellent, but she was careful not to intrude on other conversations. She was obviously well-educated and well-traveled. I sensed that it would be a treat to have a long conversation and get to know her better, but the number of guests and the wedding activities did not permit me to do so.

A few years later, my wife, Betty, and I were in Amsterdam and arranged to meet her for dinner at an elegant restaurant. I no longer remember the details of our conversation, but I remember clearly that the conversation was pleasant and stimulating. It amply fulfilled our expectations. We were pleased and proud to have her as part of our extended family.

Two or three years later, we were sorry to learn from Rogier that his grandmother had been diagnosed with lung cancer. The cancer was in her right upper lung and was incurable. This impressive and gracious woman faced a grim outlook.

The cancer was held in check for a while by X-ray treatments and chemotherapy, but after a few months it began to grow again. Worse yet, from time to time, the cancer would bleed into her air passages. Then she would cough up bright red blood. The coughing would cause more bleeding; the bleeding would cause more coughing, and so on in a vicious circle.

Once, coughing up blood and gasping for air, she had to be rushed to the hospital. A breathing tube was placed in her windpipe, and she was connected to a respirator. She vowed never to repeat that experience. It became obvious that she didn't have long to live. And she grew increasingly fearful that she would die in a fit of choking, coughing up blood and unable to get her breath. She spoke to her physician about her fears and formally requested euthanasia. After lengthy discussion and review of all the circumstances, her doctor agreed. Necessary outside consultations were obtained. The consultants concurred. A date was set.

Our Dutch son-in-law's grandmother: A cancer victim, she chose to end her life by euthanasia.

She wrote the script for her death. She wanted to

die in her own home, in her own bed. She wanted her two daughters to be by her side when her physician injected the lethal drugs into an arm vein. She wanted her two son-in-laws to be there also. She did not want any of her grandchildren to be present. Or her friends. She also spelled out her wishes for the funeral arrangements. She thought of many details, including arranging to have some valuable artworks removed to a safe storage facility immediately after her death in order not to leave them in an empty house inviting to robbers.

It all went according to plan. For her, it was a peaceful, dignified departure from the world in the presence of her most immediate family and with their love and support. It was just as she had hoped. Her family was sad, of course, but greatly relieved that she had been spared the terminal ordeal that she had feared so much.

After writing this, I wanted to double-check that my memory was accurate, so I spoke to the Dutch family. My recollection was essentially correct, but the patient's daughter offered to write down just how she recalled her mother's death and how she regards euthanasia. Verbatim, her letter reads as follows:

In 1994 my mother, 79, after exploratory surgery, was diagnosed with metastasized untreatable lung cancer. She was given a life expectancy of no more than one year. Even before the first bouts of serious coughing and periods of near asphyxiation she decided that she wanted to end her life by euthanasia. She found that her doctor was prepared to do this for her. He consulted a colleague who agreed with him that her situation qualified for euthanasia within the requirements of the law.

My mother informed her children, my sister and me,

and we agreed wholeheartedly with her decision. After almost a year passed in restful knowledge of life in her own hands and after celebrating with us and her grandchildren her 80th birthday, she set a date for her death. On that day my sister and I and our husbands sat at her bed, the doctor asked her explicitly, "Madam, do you want to proceed?" She answered, "Yes, doctor," and stretched out her arm for the injection. Immediately after the first injection she lost consciousness and very soon after the second one she died.

Afterward the doctor informed the authorities who ruled that all legal requirements had been met.

My sister and I, sad for losing our mother, were and still are glad when we look back on this dignified and self-determined death of a patient who otherwise would have suffered unbearably and hopelessly.

To the daughters and their families, euthanasia had been a blessing. I was also told that their mother's physician felt personal satisfaction in being able to spare his patients from prolonged suffering at the end of their lives.

At the end-of-life conference I attended in Amsterdam, there was an afternoon devoted to the Dutch experience with euthanasia. A documentary film traced the life and death of a patient with Lou Gehrig's disease, also known as ALS (amyotrophic lateral sclerosis). The life portrayed was one of progressive disability, with ultimate loss of almost every human function. Death by euthanasia finally seemed a blessing for both the patient and his long-suffering spouse. The film was obviously made to arouse sympathy and support for euthanasia, but it was compelling. Especially since the patient seemed sure to die before long, with a great deal of suffering in the dying process for both the patient and his wife.

There were also a number of presentations about the process, including consultation with outside, objective specialists in the relevant diseases. Psychiatric consultation was also mandatory, as was a two-week waiting period to be sure this wasn't a hasty decision. Finally, the Dutch equivalent of our district attorney had to be notified and the death investigated as though it might be a homicide. To be sure there was no financial motive for the doctor administering the fatal drugs, it is against the law to collect a fee.

Several facts stood out to me. Only 14 percent of those who signed up for euthanasia actually ended up dying from euthanasia. The great majority died of their underlying disease and natural causes. But many of those who did not follow through still found comfort in knowing that the possibility existed. Those who signed up for euthanasia actually lived longer than matched controls of similar age and disease status who did not sign up, possibly because they were relieved to know there was a way to end their suffering if it became unbearable.

I talked to several Dutch physicians, some of them found the whole process somewhat onerous. They did not look forward to carrying out a lethal injection. The process was time-consuming and emotionally troubling to many of them. The prime motive for a physician to participate was simply the desire to spare their patients a great deal of suffering from a death that was inevitable before long anyway. In general, that was enough of a motivation.

I was left with the feeling that the Dutch program was well thought out, with multiple protections to avoid its abuse. I was also sure that it was a blessing for some patients and their families. At the same time, I was left with some nagging questions for which I had no answers. Nearly every religion has a prohibition about killing. "Thou shalt not kill" is one of the Ten Commandments. It is also one of the Five Precepts of Buddhism. And so on with most other religions.

I could not visualize myself carrying out the Dutch protocol. On the other hand, I have sometimes been extremely aggressive in trying to minimize pain through high doses of narcotic: doses so high that I worried about depressing respiration and hastening death. For example, I once had a patient who had undergone a bypass arterial graft to both legs to increase blood flow and prevent gangrene. He was 65 and a chronic heavy smoker. He did very well postoperatively, but several months later he was readmitted with a swollen, bluish leg due to a blood clot. His chest X-ray showed a large cancer in his right upper lung. (Lung cancer sometimes can cause the blood to clot more easily and predispose the patient to blood clots in the legs or elsewhere.) Surgery showed that the tumor was inoperable, so it was treated with X-ray therapy and chemotherapy. The treatment was not effective. The tumor invaded the chest wall and the nerves going to the shoulder and arm, causing a great deal of pain that was hard to control.

One day the patient woke up at home with pain in both legs, which also had an alarming, unhealthy purple color. He was rushed to the hospital. It was quickly apparent that he had clotted off the graft I had put in place some months before, shutting off the circulation to the lower half of his body, particularly his pelvis and legs. Untreated, I was sure that the outcome would be gangrene and death before too long.

Gently, I tried to explain the situation to him. I said that this was an emergency, and I saw no option but to operate again to remove the clot and restore blood flow to the lower part of his body. He was quite alert and clearly understood the situation. But he said emphatically that he was not going to have another operation, no matter what the outcome. After all, he said, the cancer is going to kill me, if the blood clot doesn't.

I looked at his wife, thinking she might urge him to have the operation. She didn't. I thought for a moment. I had not been in a situation just like this before. I wondered how I would feel if I were in the patient's place. His logic seemed hard to refute: The cancer would indeed kill him, if the blood clot didn't. Also, the cancer was causing a lot of pain. I was reasonably sure that if nothing was done, the blood clot would kill him soon and that we could keep him comfortable until he died. I went over the options once more with the patient and his wife. They were adamant in refusing treatment, and I did not try to dissuade them. I thought to myself that I might make the same decision if I were in the patient's place.

To control the pain, I ordered intravenous morphine, delivered by a Patient Controlled Analgesia (PCA) infusion pump. With this Patient Controlled Analgesia, he could push a button and the pump would inject a preset dose of morphine into the intravenous tubing. After a preset delay time, the dose could be repeated. It is customary to be cautious in both the size of the dose and the frequency of the injections, in order to avoid an inadvertent overdose. However, for this patient my prime concern was to keep him comfortable. I had no idea how much morphine would be required. I had never stood by and watched, while an alert patient's lower body slowly died for lack of blood supply. I thought it might be quite painful. So I set the pump to deliver a high dose of morphine, to be repeated as often as he felt the need. Some of the nurses were upset. What was to prevent him from dying of an overdose? They had never cared for a patient who could self-administer as much intravenous morphine as he wanted.

Pain was not a problem, perhaps because of the immediate dose of morphine whenever he felt pain—and perhaps because dying tissue becomes numb before long. Without much discomfort and perhaps with a drug-induced drowsiness, the patient slept most of the time. He woke from time to time to talk briefly to his family members, who stayed by his bedside. As toxic substances from his dying leg muscles spread throughout his body, he gradually went into a deepening coma. He did not need to push the button for pain relief any longer. In about 24 hours, he died quite peacefully. The nurses were relieved. Surprisingly little morphine had been used. The wife, who was a nurse herself, was greatly relieved and almost embarrassingly grateful.

But what if he had self-administered a lethal overdose? How would I have felt then? I believe that my conscience would have been clear. I was trying, admittedly quite aggressively, to relieve pain that I assumed might be unusually severe otherwise. I was not trying to end the man's life. My intent was morally justified. There is an ethical doctrine, acceptable even to Catholic theologians, known as the "doctrine of double-effect." It states that it is morally justifiable to give large doses, even possibly life-endangering doses, of pain medications if necessary to relieve severe pain. However, it is not justifiable to give such doses with the intent of ending the patient's life. The intent of the physician is what matters.

So how do I feel about euthanasia or physician-assisted suicide? I realize that they appear to have been a blessing to some patients and their families. But I find it hard to imagine myself deliberately ending a patient's life, even apart from any moral or legal constraints. Furthermore, I have never been asked by a patient to do so. My own experience has been that with appropriate advance care planning and with aggressive comfort measures, including large doses of narcotics as necessary, the question just hasn't come up. Perhaps that is in part because of the nature of my former practice. With that question in my mind, I asked a friend who was the medical director of a busy hospice for 20 years how often he had been asked to help end a patient's life. "Only once in 20 years," he replied. "But I have been called up before the Drug Enforcement Agency three times for alleged excessive narcotic prescriptions," he was quick to add. Like me, he was aggressive in the use of narcotics to relieve pain. I asked him, "Do you think there is ever a role for physician-assisted suicide or euthanasia?"

He thought for a moment. "Perhaps in some end-stage neurological diseases. The moral issue doesn't trouble me. But with good care, the question just doesn't seem to come up in my patients."

And that is where we left it. My friend clearly felt that if palliative care is done well, there is rarely a need for physician-assisted suicide.

I have also been reassured by my limited contacts

with other physicians who employ euthanasia or physician-assisted suicide, but I am much more comfortable with the use of aggressive pain relief and expert palliative care. I also feel that, if the patient wishes, it is appropriate to withhold treatment that may prolong life but cannot restore its quality. It is also appropriate to use large doses of drugs that are necessary to relieve pain, even if they may lead to an early death. As a patient myself, I have already made those desires clear to my family and my physicians. They have promised to respect and honor my wishes.

CHAPTER 21

The Psychic

—

The last three chapters have dealt with heavy subjects: suicide, euthanasia, and physician-assisted suicide. It is time for a change of pace, something perhaps a bit lighter, but also more controversial. This chapter is about an encounter with a psychic—and the message she allegedly brought back to me from a dead relative.

The story begins with an experience of our former son-in-law, Jesse Baskir. He had met our daughter Jane when he was studying for a doctorate at Massachusetts Institute of Technology. She was getting a master's degree at the Harvard School of Public Health. After graduation they were married, and Jesse took a job with the Environmental Protection Agency in San Francisco. One night Jesse came home to their apartment in Oakland to find a frantic message on the answering machine. It was from his mother. She sounded desperate.

*Jesse, where are you?............Answer the phone, Jesse!................Please…please…PLEASE! Answer the phone!............*there was a pause, and the line went dead.

Jesse knew there must have been a terrible crisis at his family home in Houston. He knew it must involve his father, who would otherwise have taken charge in a crisis. He called home immediately. There was no answer. How could he find out what had happened? After a minute, he started calling the emergency rooms of Houston hospitals. With increasing anxiety, he asked, "Have you seen a patient named Manny Baskir?" At the third hospital he called, the ER clerk said matter-of-factly, "We had a DOA by that name." Jesse went numb. He knew what DOA meant: *Dead on Arrival.*

How could it be? His father was only 60 years old. He had no known health problems. He had even been planning to ride his bicycle in a fundraising bikeathon to Austin the next weekend. How could he possibly be dead? But it was true. Manny Baskir had suffered a sudden cardiac arrest at home. There had been no warning. No chance for Jesse to say goodbye. Or thanks. Or I love you. Jesse was profoundly upset—and he remained upset for a long time to come.

His friends and colleagues at the EPA wanted to help Jesse through this bad time. Someone suggested they all pitch in and pay for a reading with a well-known psychic in Oakland. They had heard that this psychic could carry messages from the living to the dead, and from the dead back to the living. They thought that perhaps she could contact Jesse's dad and transmit some healing messages from him to Jesse. It was worth a try, they thought. But there was a problem: Jesse did not believe in psychics, or survival of the spirit after death, or an afterlife. There was no place for such beliefs in his science-based worldview. He appreciated his friends' desire to help, but he was sure that a reading by a psychic would be a waste of his time—and his friends' money. He said thanks, but no thanks.

His friends were not easily put off. Their California worldview included psychic communication with the dead, even if the worldview of a newly minted scientist from MIT did not. They told Jesse that they had already paid the money and that it would be wasted if he didn't have the reading. They urged him to schedule an appointment, whether he believed in psychics or not. Reluctantly, he agreed, and in due course he had the reading.

Our daughter Jane said that Jesse didn't talk much about that reading afterward, even with her. He seemed comforted, but a bit unsettled by the experience. The psychic had brought warm and comforting messages that were allegedly from his father. "Manny," or whoever spoke for him, said that he was well and happy in a beautiful place. He said that he was glad to have a chance to communicate with Jesse. He wanted Jesse to know how much he appreciated Jesse's support of his mother after the sudden and unexpected death. And how much he appreciated Jesse's kind words at the memorial service. Manny's messages were uniformly positive, comforting, and loving.

Why, then, was the experience unsettling? Jane said that Jesse had trouble giving up his skepticism about the supernatural. His father's words, allegedly from the spirit world, had been credible and comforting; but they were also words that could have been conjured up by a clever charlatan. Also, some of the psychic's descriptions of his dad didn't ring true to Jesse. For example, she had described Manny wearing large eyeglasses with flip-up sunshades. Jesse said that he had never seen his dad wear flip-up sunshades and couldn't imagine him doing so.

But I had!

After Jane and Jesse's wedding in our backyard,

Betty and I invited Manny and Helene Baskir to spend a week with us on Cape Cod. We thought that it would a good way to get to know our new in-laws better. It was a pleasant week, and the weather was sunny. We spent a lot of time sitting on the deck overlooking the bay and visiting. I have a strong memory of Manny sitting on the railing of our cottage deck, wearing large eyeglasses with flip-up eyeshades! The striking similarity with the psychic's description piqued my curiosity. Betty and I had never met a psychic. We thought it should be interesting, even if the psychic was a fraud. So I asked our daughter Jane to schedule an appointment during our next visit to Oakland.

A few months later, Betty and I took a long walk on a pleasant spring day in Oakland. We started from Jane and Jesse's apartment, went halfway around Lake Merritt, and reached the large apartment building where we were going to meet the psychic. We arrived a bit early and rang the bell. There was no answer. We stood there, wondering what to do. While we were waiting, a trim and attractive woman, perhaps 45 or 50 years old, came walking briskly down the street and up the front steps of the apartment house. Her suit matched her sandy, short hair. She looked quite professional, perhaps an accountant, lawyer or office manager.

With a smile, she said, "You must be the Wheelers." I was surprised. This well-groomed woman did not fit my image of a psychic, but she quickly introduced herself as Louise Hauck, the psychic. She ushered us into a spacious atrium, going up four or five stories. It contained an old-fashioned glass cage elevator, and a broad spiral staircase that hugged the outside wall. We walked up the stairs to the second floor, admiring the space and the dated elegance of the building

Louise Hauck took us through the entry hall into her living room. Long windows flanked by heavy drapes faced the lake. I noted interesting artifacts from exotic places. I would have liked to ask about them, but we were there for other reasons. The psychic seated us side by side on a couch. Then she pulled up a chair facing us.

I asked Louise how she had become a psychic. She told us that she was born with psychic ability. Even as a small child, she could look at a stranger and see visions of that person's past and future. She said it was almost as though that person's life was captured on a reel of film that she could run forward or back in her mind. As a child, she thought that everyone had the same ability. However, when she mentioned her visions to her playmates, they thought she was just making up stories. She told her mother about her friends' reactions. Her mother said that she was also a psychic and had similar experiences as a child. She advised Louise not to talk about her insights. She said that psychic ability was a gift, but a gift that could bring problems with its use. For years Louise did not use her psychic gifts or talk about them with others; but as a young adult, she learned that she could sometimes be helpful to other people by sharing her visions of their lives. She said that she wished that her clients could see what she sees. People and places that meant nothing to Louise would be instantly meaningful to her clients, even though they might not be recognizable from her attempts to describe them.

I asked if she could contact spirits of the dead. "Sometimes," she said, "but only if they want to be contacted."

She asked if we wanted to contact some departed spirit. I said that we had no one in mind. "Well," she said, "we'll see if someone on the other side wants to contact you."

And she continued, "Do you have any personal problems? Maybe I can see something that will be helpful." After thinking for a minute, I responded that we were worried about the difficulty our youngest daughter Mary was having in getting her PhD thesis approved. After completing all her course work and receiving a tentative approval on the thesis from Cornell, Mary had moved to the Netherlands with her new Dutch husband. Her major professor had then written her, requiring belated revisions to the thesis; but the necessary resources needed to comply were not available in her small Dutch town. It seemed probable that she would not receive her degree, despite five years of hard work.

"Well, we can see what happens about that," said the psychic.

It was time to begin the reading. Louise asked us to give her some object to hold that had been in close touch with our bodies for a long time. She explained that it would help her to tune into our psychic wavelength. I don't wear bracelets, chains, or other jewelry, so she suggested my wristwatch. Betty also gave her wristwatch to the psychic. With a watch in each hand, Louise closed her eyes and began to meditate, presumably getting in touch with our life histories, past and future. After two or three minutes, with her eyes still closed and appearing almost asleep, she began to describe scenes and people flitting across her field of consciousness. "There is an older man here. His name starts with the letter *L*. Is it Larry? Leonard? Luke?"

My dead grandfather Vance was named Leslie, but I was not impressed. Images did not seem to be coming easily to Louise. She seemed to be looking to us for clues. Or was that negative first impression just my natural skepticism?

"Now about your daughter's problem with her thesis," she abruptly continued. "There is no problem. I see an older man being very helpful. All that will be necessary is to revise the order in which the thesis material is presented—like shuffling a deck of cards. It will not be a problem."

That seemed highly unlikely to me, after everything we had heard about the demands of the thesis committee at Cornell. I was not reassured.

After the reading, as time went by, I nearly forgot all about the psychic's confident prediction. But several months later, Mary received an unexpected letter from an older man, Professor Grossvogel, the chairman of her thesis committee. He was very helpful. He said that all that the thesis needed was to revise the order of the chapters: like shuffling a deck of cards. He even said that since Mary was living in Europe, Cornell would waive the usual thesis defense. In short, there was no problem, just as the psychic had confidently predicted—and despite all my doubts.

During the meeting, the psychic also described a spirit who was anxious to give me a message. The spirit was an older woman whose dark hair was liberally sprinkled with gray. She was short and a bit heavy, with a friendly face and a quick smile. She was pictured in her kitchen, cooking in a print dress with an apron. Colorful flowers from her garden were on the table. As the psychic's description became more detailed, I suddenly realized that the image was of my Aunt Vivian. She had died of stomach cancer several years before.

Louise eyes remained closed, and her speech became softer. She seemed to be in a deeper trance state as she described my aunt. Then, with more urgency, the psychic said, "She is quite anxious to give you a message. She wants you to know how happy she was about the three-way split."

This strange message—from who knows where—gave me a strong jolt. It seemed to have the ring of truth. For a reader to understand why, I have to share some family history:

Tuberculosis was once common in eastern Kentucky; and my father's mother, Elizabeth Lemaster Wheeler, contracted the disease in her teens. By the time she was 28, and the mother of two small children, she was dying of "consumption." My father was about six years old at that time and my Aunt Vivian was only two or three, when their mother died.

A few years later, their father remarried. He needed a wife. The children needed a mother. And the farm needed a woman to keep the house, can the fruits and vegetables, look after the henhouse, milk the cow, and cook for the family and any hired hands brought in for spring planting or fall harvesting. In short, to do the innumerable jobs that occupied farm women from early morning until late at night. As soon as they were able, the children were pressed into service as well.

The new wife was also named Elizabeth, but she

was always known around the farm as Lizzie. As far as I know, Lizzie provided adequately for the basic needs of her now motherless stepchildren, but I am sure that they never received the same warmth and love that they might have received from their own mother. Lizzie had a stern streak and wasn't big on hugs and kisses. She had a hard life herself and didn't think that children were immune from working. In time, Lizzie had two boys of her own. Understandably, with two young children of her own, her older stepchildren dropped a notch or two lower in her priorities.

Without their own mother and with a father who, like most farmers in Appalachia at that time, was taciturn, stern, and emotionally unexpressive, my father and his sister, Vivian, were drawn closer to each other. My father was always quick to help his little sister, and she looked up to him in return. There was something quite different and special about their relationship. Perhaps the loss of their mother in early childhood made them more sensitive to the emotional needs of others. For whatever reason, they both had an unusual empathy for the problems of other people.

Aunt Vivian received no education beyond public school. She had no female role model and no personal ambition. She never left Paintsville. She married a kind and honest man, Greenville Helton. He had a farming background, but had come to find work in the town. Vivian and Greenville never had any children. During the Depression, they worked at whatever jobs they could find. They always found work, usually working together in the same place. My aunt was smart, conscientious, hard working, and quite good with people. She was calm and friendly and quickly found a common sense solution to most problems. She did well with whatever she undertook, whether running the office of the Paintsville Funeral Home, managing rental property, or starting her own business, the Helton Maytag Store. She and her husband ran this appliance store successfully for many years. As they prospered, my aunt and uncle were able to purchase a small farm near town. They both loved to garden, mainly vegetables but also flowers for the house. They kept a horse and chickens and hounds that my uncle used for bird hunting. They led a simple life, ate food they had produced themselves or gotten from my grandfather's farm; and they did enough physical work to get some healthy exercise. So, it came as a shock when Aunt Vivian walked into the living room one day and found Greenville sitting in his favorite rocking chair with his chin on his chest ... dead.

My Aunt Vivian and Uncle Greenville: She delivered a convincing message to me through a psychic.

Greenville's will gave everything he owned to Vivian. It wasn't all that much. She lived on for a few years but developed cancer of the stomach. The surgeon who operated on her told me that the cancer had spread beyond what he could remove, and I knew her death was only a matter of time. I tried to talk to her by phone more frequently, and I felt guilty that I couldn't do more.

After a brief downhill course, she died. After the funeral and burial, it was time to settle her modest estate, but no one could find her will. We thought that if Greenville had made a will, surely Vivian had too. Her half-brother, John Martin Wheeler, searched all the obvious places, but no will was ever found. So, in accordance with the laws of Kentucky, a two-year mandatory waiting period passed before the estate could be settled. By that time, my father was in his nineties. The long trip from his home in Nashville to eastern Kentucky was too much for him. My brother, a pediatrician who also lived in Nashville, was given power of attorney and went to represent our family.

The families of my father's two half-brothers were also involved. Neither of these men had pursued education beyond the public schools. One sold family bibles door to door in the coal mining country of West Virginia. It was a subsistence living. He died before Aunt Vivian did and left two children with no more money than he'd had. The other half-brother was a salesman who sold supplies to hardware stores. I doubt that he earned much. As a devout convert to the Mormon faith, he almost certainly gave the Mormon Church a tenth of his income.

When time finally came to settle the estate, the lawyer explained that under the laws of Kentucky it would be divided in equal shares among the next of kin or their descendants. However, the two half-brothers would each only get half a share, whereas my father would get a full share. This division of the estate troubled my brother, acting as my father's agent. He called me and said, "Brownell, this is the situation. Daddy is entitled to a full share of Aunt Vivian's estate, but Uncle Roy's family and Uncle John Martin are only entitled to one-half a share. If I talk to Daddy, he will probably take the full share, to which he is entitled, not because he needs it or wants it, but because he would want us to have it.

"Daddy is in his nineties. He has enough to get by. He doesn't need the money. You and I are doctors. We don't really need the money either. We will have enough to meet our needs. Brownell, these other two families have little. It means a lot to them. My inclination is simply to split the estate three ways and not even tell Daddy that his share could have been double what the others received. What do you think?"

I was proud of my brother. I agreed with him. Aunt Vivian's estate was split in three equal shares. We never told my father.

—

Louise Hauck opened her eyes slowly. She had been in a trance for nearly an hour. Turning her head to look directly into my eyes, she said slowly, "What was … that business … about a three-way split?" Without waiting for an answer, and speaking more slowly still, she said dreamily, "Did that … mean something … to you?"

"Yes," I said, "it meant quite a lot, actually. But it would take a long time to explain."

I hesitated to say that the message about the three-way split came from Aunt Vivian. Now, from some unknown place in space and time, she appeared to have used Louise's psychic abilities to tell me how happy she was about the equal distribution of her estate. How otherwise could the psychic have known about the three-way split? It was an obscure bit of family history that I had nearly forgotten myself. How could she read my mind, if my mind was empty?

CHAPTER 22

The Transience of Tennis Partners

—

When Betty and I moved to Worcester, it took me some time to find new tennis partners. But after a year or two, I settled into a routine with one singles game and one doubles each week.

Playing tennis, 1973

One of the things I liked most about tennis was the opportunity it provided me to get out of the medical world and meet people from all walks of life. My regular doubles partners were a fireman, an engineer, and an insurance adjuster. My regular singles partner was Paul Bedard, a fifth-grade teacher in his mid-forties, about my own age. I liked the fact that Paul taught elementary school children: It said something good about his values.

Paul had done a lot of physical labor in his life, and he still worked in his spare time finishing floors. He carried a heavy floor sander in his car. I was impressed with how heavy it was, and Paul's muscular arms and shoulders did not surprise me. His brown hair was thinning and turning gray, which perhaps motivated him to wear a salt-and-pepper beard. He wore large eyeglasses with dark plastic rims.

After two or three sets of singles, the score of which could go either way, Paul and I would shower and go to a nearby bar for a beer and a visit. I liked talking to Paul. It took me out of my medical world into a different lifestyle and a different set of concerns.

After playing with Paul for several years, I was surprised to hear him talk of retiring and moving to Maine. Although only in his fifties, he would soon have taught for 30 years. With that length of service, he was eligible for a full retirement, even before reaching the age of 60. He and his wife, Arlene, began to make plans to live in a mobile home community just over the Maine border. But shortly before they moved, a frightening thing happened.

He and Arlene were vacationing in Florida, relaxing on a beach. Without warning, Paul slumped over, unconscious, and unresponsive to Arlene's frantic cries. Fortunately, a man sunning on the sand nearby had been trained in CPR. He carried out forceful chest compressions; and Paul came to, groggy, but alive. He was taken by ambulance to the nearest hospital. An Electrocardiogram (EKG) showed no evidence of a heart attack, and a cardiac catheterization showed no blockage of the coronary arteries.

The cause of his sudden and near-fatal collapse on the beach was unclear. It was ascribed to an unexplained cardiac arrhythmia, a furiously rapid and ineffective beating of the heart muscle. He was placed on anti-arrhythmic medication and referred back to UMass Medical Center for further work-up.

At UMass, Paul's initial studies were all normal, except for a slower than normal pulse rate, which is not uncommon in athletes in top condition. Bjorn Borg, the best tennis player in the world at that time, was reported to have a resting pulse rate as slow as 35 beats per minute, about half the normal rate. Having a slow pulse rate makes a person more apt than usual to have extra heartbeats from time to time, as well as more serious disorders of cardiac rhythm. These events are short-lived and sporadic, so a random EKG lasting only a minute or two may not reveal them, whereas a continuous EKG over 24 hours may show several rhythm disturbances and allow a diagnosis to be made. Paul's cardiologist ordered a Holter monitor—a small, portable, battery-operated EKG machine—to record his heartbeat throughout the day.

The day of the Holter test, Paul went for a walk of about three miles. After his walk, Paul sat down in his favorite easy chair to read the paper. A few minutes later, he slumped back in the chair, unconscious. Arlene was frantic. Paul was unresponsive. She did not know how to do CPR. Desperate, she called 911. After what seemed an eternity, EMTs rushed in, started CPR, placed Paul on a stretcher, and took off at high speed for the nearest hospital, siren screaming. At the ER, the hospital staff worked frantically for over an hour, but Paul never responded. His heart had just been stopped for too long.

The Holter monitor was in place until the resuscitation efforts were well underway. Later, I was given the tracing to review. It told the whole story. Paul's heart was beating strongly and regularly throughout his long walk and when he first sat down to rest and read the paper. But the rate was slow. Because of the slow rate, there were occasional extra heartbeats. One of these random extra beats occurred at the precise moment, only a split-second long, when the heart is most sensitive and vulnerable. In Paul's case, the overreaction made his heart muscle twitch and quiver, continuously and ineffectively, rather than contract forcefully to pump out blood beat by beat. In situations like this, without effective pumping action by the heart, the brain receives no oxygen and the patient collapses. Unless an effective heartbeat can be restored within a few minutes, the patient dies—even if he is otherwise in top shape, as Paul had been. Paul's autopsy showed no heart disease—or any other disease.

I was shocked to learn of Paul's death. He was not yet 60 years old. He had just retired and had always seemed healthy and strong. He was looking forward to having time to do vigorous outdoor activities for many years. And it all seemed so unnecessary! Why did the fatal extra beat occur precisely at the one brief instant that Paul's heart was most vulnerable? Why hadn't his wife been taught CPR? Why did it take all of 18 minutes, documented on the Holter monitor tape, for the EMTs to arrive? Why? Why? Why?

I went to the funeral home to pay my respects to Paul and to offer my condolences to Arlene and the children. The funeral home was a white frame house that had been renovated to provide space for calling hours and small funerals. The front door opened into a large living room that contained a few chairs and a casket surrounded by flowers. The casket was open. Reluctantly, I looked at the pale face of my longtime friend. And unexpectedly, I burst into tears. The eyeglasses were what got me. Paul was wearing his reading glasses! A dead man was wearing glasses that he would never use. His eyelids were closed, as though he was tired of reading and was just resting his eyes. I half-expected those eyes to open at any moment. It seemed so natural, but so out of place in the funeral home.

Arlene sensed my confusion. She came over and explained that when she first saw Paul in the casket, he didn't look like the man she loved. For most of their life together she had been used to seeing Paul wear eyeglasses. So she went home and got his current pair of glasses and put them on him. It made him seem much more natural to her.

I was also surprised to see a black-beaded rosary in Paul's hands, as though he were saying his prayers. Paul and I had had many deep conversations after our tennis games, facilitated by large mugs of draft beer. I remembered Paul as having been curious as to what I believed or didn't believe about religion. Or about psychic matters, such as ghosts, mediums, and an afterlife. He didn't say as much about his own beliefs. But I had the distinct impression that he had rejected the Catholic dogma of his childhood. I doubted that he ever went to Mass, let alone say the rosary. So I assumed the beads were Arlene's idea. I hoped in some way they comforted her. It would be nice to think of Paul on some heavenly tennis court, I thought. His backhand would doubtless improve.

Two other tennis partners of mine also died suddenly and unexpectedly. One about 40 years old collapsed and died playing a semifinal match in a club tennis tournament. Another, in his sixties, had a heart attack while sailing his boat. I am only too well aware of the fragile and unpredictable nature of life, on and off the tennis court. Of course, this is a lesson I have learned and relearned in the practice of medicine. But having healthy, athletic friends die suddenly and unexpectedly is different. It sears the fragile nature of life on your heart. Why Paul? Why Dave? Why Nikki? ... Why not me?

CHAPTER 23

The Channel Medium

—

My professional life required me to attend a lot of meetings, one of which was the annual Surgical Research Laboratory party. One year the party was at the recently purchased home of my lab director, Dr. Fred Anderson. The house was a traditional New England farmhouse, but it had been modified extensively over the years. It was said to be the oldest house in Worcester, dating back to the early 1700s. Inside, a trapdoor led to a hidden room in the cellar, originally built as an escape from Indian attacks. Before and during the Civil War, runaway slaves took refuge in the room, a regular stop on the underground railway.

As guests for the party began to arrive, the talk turned to Fred's newly acquired house and its history that included Indian attacks and runaway slaves. Fred's wife, Dale, remarked that the house was haunted. By whom, we asked? A settler killed by the Indians? A child killed by diphtheria or whooping cough? A woman who died in childbirth? A runaway slave who died of disease incurred during a long and desperate flight to freedom?

"Have you seen the ghost?" someone eagerly asked Dale.

"No, but we've only lived here a week." Her reply implied that she fully expected to see the ghost later.

"You don't believe in ghosts, do you?" The question-er clearly anticipated a negative answer.

"Yes, I do. I have seen ghosts," she told the group of surgeons, biomedical engineers, and other young scientists.

The room was suddenly quiet.

"Really?" The question implied disbelief.

So our hostess told the group about a house she had lived in as a child and a ghost that she had seen there on several occasions. That ghost was well known to people who had lived there. I have forgotten her ghost story. What I do remember clearly is how this ghost testimonial from our hostess opened up the evening for others to recount their own encounters with supernatural and paranormal events.

The fiancée of one of our lab staff was a strong-looking young man with long, black hair pulled back in a ponytail. He was introduced as a Native American shaman, and his Indian name was Day Lone Wolf. He told us about the spirit world beliefs of his tribe and how a person could visit the spirit world by participating in certain rituals. Some rituals involved smoking peyote. Other rituals involved use of a sweat lodge or dancing and drumming. The world of spirits and ghosts began to seem quite real. The shaman finished his story by asking if we would like to see his pet wolf.

There was an excited murmur. "Do you really have a wolf? ... Here?"

And yes, it turned out he had a wolf in his pickup truck. Day told us to sit in a large circle, but to leave a large opening so the wolf could enter or leave the room with ease. A wolf must never feel surrounded or boxed in, that it must always see a way to escape easily.

And so the wolf was brought into the house with Day's hand on his back. It was one of the most impressive and frightening animals that I have ever seen. It was the size of a very large dog—lean and lithe and muscular—an efficient-looking killing machine, like a shark or a panther or some other well-designed predator. It must have been an arctic wolf because it was nearly white with large, yellow eyes that looked restlessly here and there, always ending at the circle's opening—the animal's emergency path out of the house. This was not an animal that you were tempted to pet. You might lose a hand. After the Indian shaman told us a bit about the animal's history, and after everyone had a good look, he led the wolf back out to the truck. We all breathed a bit easier.

The ice had been broken on talking about the strange and unusual. No subject was taboo, and the theme of the night unexpectedly turned out to be the supernatural. Another young man spoke up. He was an engineer, the fiancée of a young woman, Lauren, who was a bioengineering student doing a research project in my lab. The work would be the basis for her PhD dissertation. I was a faculty member on her thesis advisory committee. Her PhD degree required my approval. I was sure Lauren's fiancée would never say something in my presence that reflected badly on her. And what he had to say was certainly something that I might have doubted, if I had had any doubt at all about the honesty of the person saying it.

"Well, I've had an interesting paranormal experience too," he said. "My sister has become a channel medium."

"What's a channel medium?" several people asked

at once.

"Well, I can't define it exactly, but I can tell you what happens. My sister closes her eyes and concentrates on her breathing, which becomes quite slow and shallow. Then, suddenly, her eyes open and she speaks to whoever is there, but it's no longer my sister speaking. Somebody else speaks through her, sometimes a man, sometimes a woman. But I know it's not my sister speaking. I know my sister too well. She would never try to fool me. She couldn't, if she tried. And I know it's not my sister's voice. The words aren't my sister's words. And whoever is speaking knows things that my sister has no way of knowing. ... Isn't that weird?"

Yes, that was weird, we all agreed. We asked many questions: Who is speaking through your sister? Why? How did she find out she could do this? And so on.

His responses sketched out the bare outline of a story: His sister had seen another channel medium somewhere. That medium said she could also be a medium. The purpose of a medium was to allow the spirit world to communicate information that was potentially helpful to people in this world. These disembodied, "discarnate" spirits might be called ghosts or angels or simply spirits. They communicate through the body of a channel medium. His sister regarded this function as a service to others, a ministry of sorts, and she spending much of her time trying to help anyone who wished to contact a wise and helpful spirit from some other world.

When the party finally began to break up later, I spoke to the young man whose sister was the medium. Was it possible for me or my wife to contact his sister? It turned out not to be easy. She lived in Steamboat Springs,

Colorado. However, each year she came east to see her family. Perhaps we could schedule a time then. It was a strange request on my part, something that would never have happened if I hadn't gone to what at first seemed like a professionally obligatory dinner party. I had heard of channel mediums before, but I had never taken them seriously. I probably never would have, except for the honest, sincere face of the young engineering student vouching for his sister's honesty.

And so it happened that a few months later, Betty and I found ourselves one sunny afternoon, sitting in the pleasant living room of a middle-class home and waiting for the channel medium to appear. We had no idea what to expect.

"Hi! I'm Mary Ellen, Bob's sister." The words almost preceded the speaker into the room. She was a friendly young woman with a pleasant smile, in her early or mid-thirties, slightly on the plump side, medium height, and with dark hair. She looked like a suburban housewife. We chatted for a while. She had two young children, it turned out. We talked briefly about her brother, his fiancée and her connection with my research lab. Before long, she said, "Well, I know you're here to see if the spirits have anything to say to you. Shall we see?"

Yes, we were eager to see whatever came next. Mary Ellen explained briefly how she got into doing these "readings" and how the process worked. A few years ago, she had had a reading from another medium. The spirit-voice of that medium had told her that she was able to be a channel medium herself and that this would be a worthwhile calling for her, one that would benefit others. At first, she was apprehensive, but after a few introductory attempts, she began doing readings for close friends and family. As she grew in confidence, she started doing readings for strangers as well, and she concluded that being a medium was indeed a worthwhile calling for her. She had given up her previous job and started charging for the channeling sessions to make up for the lost income. (We paid $75 for an hour-and-a-half session.)

The procedure, she explained, would be as follows. She would start a tape recorder so that we would have a record of whatever was said, to replay and think about later. Then she would close her eyes and meditate. She would meditate on turning over her will to a higher power so that benign spirits might be of help to those seeking it. At some point, probably after a few minutes had gone by, she would feel her body being taken over by a spirit. She would hear that spirit speaking through her body, but would only be a passive observer, taking no part in the dialogue between the spirit and the seeker. Her eyes would be open, her face might even be animated, but her appearance would reflect the spirit, not herself. Sometimes the appearance of the spirit startled people, but we should not be alarmed, the spirits were there only to do good. Nothing bad could happen to us or to her, the medium.

I listened intently to what she was saying, but the whole scene seemed unreal to me. It wasn't so much that I doubted her sincerity, but that the idea of talking to a discarnate spirit speaking through the body of a living person seemed unreal to me. My view of the world simply didn't include such possibilities.

"I should warn you of one other thing," Mary Ellen said. "When I do these sessions, my eyes are open while the spirits are speaking. I have been told that I never blink. So after a while my eyes may get dry and irritated. Tears may run down my cheeks. Sometimes my clients are worried that my eyes may be damaged or that I am suffering in some way. Please, don't worry. My eyes are fine. I'm not suffering. Believe me, there's nothing to be afraid of, for you or for me."

I found this surprising, but somehow validating. Blinking your eyes is not a conscious action. It is under the control of the autonomic nervous system, an automatic function of the body. Most of us couldn't deliberately stop blinking, even if our lives depended on it. If Mary Ellen really didn't blink during these sessions, she must indeed be in some other place, I thought.

"Shall we begin?" We nodded, yes. The tape was started. Mary Ellen sat back in her chair and closed her eyes. Her breathing slowed down and became shallow. She had a peaceful expression on her face that seemed to say, everything is all right. But I wasn't at all sure where we were headed.

Suddenly, she sat bolt upright.

"And how may we serve thee?"

The voice was loud and masculine. In fact, Mary Ellen's whole appearance was masculine. Everything about her was different: the voice, the manner, the body language, even the facial expression. I had no doubt whatever that an entirely different person suddenly confronted us. But who? And what to make of the archaic language? I had only heard the expression "thee" used in the King James Bible or old English literature.

We were stunned into a shocked silence. Finally, rather timidly, I said, "Perhaps you could tell us? How do you help others?"

Usually, he responded, others have some problem for which they need advice. The tone was warm, friendly, and helpful. I was encouraged. Perhaps, I said, it would be helpful to us to know to whom we were speaking. The speaker said that he was one of a group of 12 spirits, currently living in another world. Their task in that world was to work as a team to help people master the lessons they were on Earth to learn. They did so sometimes through dreams or planting thoughts in people's minds, but it was especially helpful to be able to talk to people directly. They could only do that through the body of a willing medium. Most of the 12 spirits had lived on Earth before, but not all. They had knowledge of other worlds — past, present, and future. They might be thought of as "advanced souls" in some way, but they still had their own lessons to learn. Serving others was one such lesson. They were only here on Earth to do good.

By this time, we were feeling a bit more comfortable with our strange visitor. I kept trying to place his language and accent. As nearly as I could pin it down, he was speaking the English of Elizabethan times or thereabouts. We asked for advice about our children.

Our new spirit friend was so specific and so accurate with respect to our children that we asked about our own lives. "You must understand," our spirit guide said, "that you have many lives until the necessary lessons are learned and the Earth plane is transcended." The medium said that Betty had had some pretty tough past lives. She had been a Native American woman in the Southwest, particularly interested in her garden and her weaving. She had been a temple dancer in India centuries ago. She had been an Eskimo woman in a particularly difficult life. These and other lives were of course unverifiable. Still, they rang true. Betty loves her garden and has been a weaver. She loves the world of nature and the beliefs of Native Americans. She is a natural dancer and loves to dance. She is empathetic to Hindu beliefs, music, and mythology. And she is from Maine and much prefers cold weather and northern climates to hot climates. For example, she was anxious to go canoeing and live for a week in the woods with the Cree Indians in northern Canada, not far from the Eskimos.

I was told that I had often been a teacher and a tribal leader in past lives—generally positive past lives, but by no means famous or especially noteworthy. The medium said I had had a female incarnation "with many children." It occurred in "Lemuria," an ancient civilization in a now-lost continent in the South Pacific—if I remember correctly.

All responses to our questions were clear, quick, and definitive. There was no hesitancy, no fumbling for words, no doubt. The answers appeared to be quite objective and factual — but totally unverifiable. However, somehow it seemed surprisingly believable under the strange circumstances. I was sure that Mary Ellen was not making it all up on the spur of the moment. I was also sure that Mary Ellen was not even part of the dialogue. To my great surprise (and Betty's), I felt that the speaker was just what he said he was, a helpful spirit from a world beyond our own.

We had run out of questions. We were more or less numb. We thanked whomever we were talking to — we still weren't sure—for his help in understanding our children and ourselves and our world and his. He smiled (through Mary Ellen's face) and bade us farewell and blessings. His eyes closed. The session was over.

Mary Ellen looked as though we had just wakened her from a sound sleep. She commented on some of the session, but apparently had not been aware of most of it. We said our thanks, took our tape, and left the house awed by our experience.

Later, I wished that I had asked all sorts of bigger questions. If I was truly talking to a highly evolved soul from some advanced spirit plane, why hadn't I asked the big metaphysical questions: Is there a God? If so, what is God's nature? And so on. I felt that I had missed a remarkable and unexpected opportunity. But that would come again, another time.

A year later, Mary Ellen came back from Colorado for her annual visit to her New England family. Once again, we arranged a session. This time I was prepared. I had thought through all my metaphysical questions: Is there a God? If so, what is the nature of God? Is there an afterlife? If so, what is its nature? What is the purpose of life on Earth? Which religions are true, at least in part, and which are false? And so on. Like a compulsive patient with many health questions, anxious to have the doctor answer each and every question, I wrote them all down, so that I would be sure not to forget.

The day of Mary Ellen's visit finally arrived. Again we were seated in the living room of her relatives. Again the brief but pleasant socializing. Again the tape recorder was started. And again Mary Ellen closed her eyes and began to meditate. This time it seemed almost familiar and even vaguely comforting. I was full of anticipation.

My question list was firmly in hand.

"How may I help?" The voice was soft and gentle. I was surprised. I had expected the forceful male voice and the masculine facial expressions of our earlier experience. The dialect and the archaic words were gone. We were obviously meeting a new spirit. This spirit was definitely quite feminine. The voice, the facial expressions, the body language were all female. Comforting. Pleasant. Warm and friendly, but with a sense of distance from the questioner. Was she a highly evolved spirit from some advanced plane of existence? I wasn't sure. I had been greatly impressed by the other spirit. This one was new to me. Could she answer my questions?

"I expected to be talking to someone else," I said with a touch of disappointment in my voice.

"We work together in a group. You can talk to me. How can I help?"

I explained that I had hoped to get some answers to life's big questions. Rather tentatively, I gathered my courage and finally said that I would like to know if there was a God and, if so, what was God like?

For a long minute, there was no response. My new spirit guide studied my face through Mary Ellen's eyes. Her look was gentle and perhaps just faintly amused. It was the kindly look of a kindergarten teacher when a five-year-old asks why the sky is blue: a question that the teacher knows how to answer, but also knows that the child is not prepared to understand her answer. Finally, she spoke. I will always remember her words.

Slowly, softly, but with great emphasis, she said gently, *"You are trying to rationalize that which is not rational."*

And after a pause, she continued, *"You are not here to explain life, but to experience it."*

Her words seemed wise to me, even profound. In a way, I felt put down. However, the put down was so gentle, so well intended, and so appropriate that I felt no resentment. Rather I felt that she was absolutely right. The metaphysical world is not subject to rational dissection and analysis. We are not here to explain it. (Much later, reading about the Buddha, I learned that he would never answer metaphysical questions, such as the existence of God, either pro or con. He called such questions "unskillful means" and emphasized practical life experience instead of philosophic speculation. It was a lesson that I had learned earlier from this channel medium.)

Somewhat chastened, I put away my list of questions. Without regret, I felt that in a way, they had all been answered. I still do. I realize that in a cosmic sense, I am at best a kindergarten student. There are many things I will never know for sure—certainly not in this life. And I have stopped fretting about it. The world has many mysteries. Some will doubtless be solved by scientific study. But behind each mystery that can be unmasked stands a more profound mystery waiting to be solved. *Thank you, Mary Ellen, for being a channel for the spirit world. And thank you, "kindergarten teacher"... whoever you may be ... wherever you may be ... for sharing your insight and perspective.*

The concept of a channel medium had been light years outside my science-based worldview. I would never have scheduled a session with a channel medium, except that a young engineer associated with my research lab said that his sister had become a channel medium, and he vouched for her credibility so earnestly. I am glad that he did. I am still surprised that we had such a credible firsthand experience.

As Hamlet said to his friend Horatio after seeing his father's ghost: "There are more things in heaven and earth, Horatio, than this world dreams of."

CHAPTER 24

The Religious Scholar

—

We had waited a long time for a new minister at the First Parish in Portland, Maine. This Unitarian Universalist church was founded in 1674. A cut-glass chandelier in the sanctuary holds a cannon ball fired at the church from Portland Harbor by a British warship during the War of 1812. Henry Wadsworth Longfellow and his family had a pew up front. The state constitution was drafted in the sanctuary.

Finally, the search committee invited a promising candidate for a weeklong interview. If all went well, at the end of the week, the congregation would vote to offer the position to our new minister. The advance word from the search committee was that the candidate they selected was exceptionally well-qualified. Their first priority, based on a membership survey, was to find a minister who would give thought-provoking, inspiring sermons.

The candidate selected, the Reverend Dr. Timothy Ward Jensen, had a rich and diverse academic background. He was a graduate of Harvard Divinity School and had no less than five degrees, including a PhD in history and an MA in creative writing. He seemed a sure bet to deliver thought-provoking sermons.

On the personal side, he had been married to a highly successful West Coast attorney; but he was now amicably divorced, presumably because of irreconcilable career conflicts with his wife. They remained close friends. He had lived most of his life on the West Coast, primarily in Washington and Oregon.

My first chance to meet the Rev. Jensen came at a church supper. Betty and I had looked forward to meeting our new minister. I don't remember any expectations on our part other than that the candidate selected had an impressive academic background. Whatever we had expected, we were quite surprised by our first meeting with him.

Tim Jensen was about 50 years old and had a large and imposing figure. He was over six feet tall and must have weighed 250 pounds. He was wearing a Boston Red Sox T-shirt and a Red Sox baseball cap over close-cut, reddish-brown hair, which matched his ruddy complexion. In one hand, he held a short leash attached to the collar of a small black-and-white Boston terrier with bulging eyes. The dog was in a place that was strange to him, with people he did not know, and he was uncomfortable. Tim kept reaching down to pet the little dog that he called Parker, after a famous Unitarian minister of the 19th century. I wondered how the original Rev. Parker would feel about the way in which his name had been perpetuated. *This minister should be interesting*, I thought. And Tim Jensen proved, indeed, to be an interesting minister, but not in the way I expected.

Tim's sermons reflected his knowledge of history and literature, as well as theology; and they appealed to many in the congregation. He quickly established personal ties with many of his new parishioners. The church seemed stable at last. But without warning one Sunday morning, Tim Jensen gave one of the most unexpected and remarkable statements from the pulpit that I have ever heard. After a few opening words of a sermon that I have long since forgotten, he suddenly digressed and spoke extemporaneously:

I have developed a little cough. At first, I didn't think much about it, but then I coughed up blood a few times. I knew that was a symptom that I shouldn't ignore, so I saw my doctor. He ordered a chest X-ray and told me later that it showed a mass about the size of an orange in the upper part of my right lung. Some tests later showed the presence of cancer cells. Surgery is probably not indicated, or so I have been told. I need to have some further studies. I may be out for a while for X-ray treatment and chemotherapy. I will keep you all informed on my blog. I look forward to continuing as your minister.

I was stunned. As a doctor, I knew what that medical scenario meant: lung cancer, with a greatly limited life expectancy, probably less than a year. And Tim was just turning 50. I had also heard before that Tim's mother had died of lung cancer within the last year. I wondered if Tim knew the full implications of what he had been told and what he was sharing with all of us. I wondered how many members of the congregation knew. I had never before heard anyone announce his death sentence to a church congregation, most of whom were new acquaintances and others total strangers.

At the coffee hour after the church service, I told Tim how sorry I was to hear of his medical problems. I also said that, as a retired surgeon, if I could answer any questions or help in any other way, I would be glad to do so. Tim seemed grateful and suggested that we meet for lunch in a quiet and confidential setting.

We met for the first of those lunches at DiMillo's, a floating restaurant on the Portland waterfront. After we had ordered our meals, I waited for Tim to tell me what medical questions were on his mind. I assumed he would be glad to have the undivided attention of a former medical school professor. I knew that often patients don't understand all that they have been told by their doctor, especially when it is frightening information about a life-threatening illness like cancer. Often, they think later about questions they wish they had asked their physician.

Although I had thought Tim might want to talk further about his illness with a medical friend, it soon became apparent that Tim just wanted to talk about anything else than his diagnosis. We talked about the restaurant, about the food, about the church, about the news of the day, about the weather, about the history of Western civilization, about English literature, about Unitarian history, about philosophy: in short, about anything and everything except his cancer. He knew far more than I about most of the topics he wanted to discuss. He was highly intelligent, naturally curious, and remarkably well-read. He liked to explain things, even to an audience of one. I learned a lot from Tim.

Over many years of delivering bad news to patients, I had learned to take my cues from the patient. When time permitted, and when I had shared the information necessary for informed consent, I let the patient control the topic of conversation. Often they were not ready to talk about their illness. Too much threatening information too soon could emotionally devastate many patients. But sometimes they were full of questions. It was hard to predict how best to handle discussions of bad news. The patient needs to know the big picture but still be left with some hope. At the end of our first lunch, Tim had barely mentioned his lung cancer; but he said that he had greatly enjoyed our talk and would like to meet again.

So began the first of many lunches with Tim. With time, I came to regard Tim as a friend who had much to give, as well as receive. I liked to think that he felt the same way about me. I was encouraged to think so when he said one day that he would like to show me his sanctum sanctorum, his private library.

We had just finished a sandwich at one of Tim's favorite lunch spots, the Top of the East. This bar and lounge atop the 12-story Eastland Hotel, the highest building in Portland, had spectacular views in all directions. To the east was Casco Bay and its many islands. To the south was a working waterfront with fishing boats, ferries, tankers, cruise ships, and, in warm weather, sailboats, ranging from small sloops to two-mast windjammers.

Also to the south was Spring Point Ledge Lighthouse. The huge granite boulders of its long causeway protected the entrance to the harbor from storms, while farther down the shore stood the familiar shape of Portland Head Light, originally commissioned by George Washington in 1792. To the west and north, on a clear day you could see the White Mountains. The tallest of the Presidential Range, Mount Washington, was covered with snow much of the year. The Top of the East was a great place to have a beer and a BLT while enjoying the panorama and a relaxed conversation.

The Eastland was a large hotel but old and dingy inside. The management could no longer fill its rooms with high-paying transient visitors, so they leased some of their floors to long-term tenants. Tim was one of these tenants. He took me on the elevator to the fifth floor where we got out onto a long and dimly lit corridor with little sign of any other tenants. We stopped in front of a door that was unmarked, except for the room number. Tim pulled out a large string of keys, found the right one, and ushered me into his *sanctum sanctorum*. I had no idea what to expect. He had told me that his personal library was too large for his church office or his home apartment, so he had rented a room in a residential hotel.

At first glance, Tim's hideaway looked like a basement storage room for a secondhand bookstore. It was crammed full of self-assembled metal shelves about six feet high. All the shelves were filled with books. There were books about the history of Unitarianism, religious history, and world history. It was easy to believe that Tim had a PhD in history. There were also many books on English literature, from Chaucer and Shakespeare to Annie Dillard and Alan Ginsberg. There were many volumes on philosophy, psychology, and theology. It was a remarkably diverse collection.

"Are all these books yours?" I asked Tim.

"All 7,000," he said with some pride.

I wondered if he was kidding—7,000 books! I could not imagine anyone owning that many books. Still, the evidence was all around me. Whatever the exact number, Tim had an unbelievably large personal library.

"Have you read them all?"

"Pretty much. Some are reference books that I just

use for a specific quote. Many are useful in writing my sermons."

I picked out a few books that I had read and asked Tim about them. I quickly learned that he knew the books far better than I did. He would have been a great college professor, with an impressive store of knowledge in several fields. I left Tim's personal library convinced that he was a true scholar.

Shortly after that visit, his illness progressed quickly. For some time, Tim had suffered from a troublesome backache. As his medical evaluation progressed, an MRI showed a collapsed lumbar vertebra, almost certainly due to spread of the lung cancer to his spine. With time, the collapsed vertebra became more and more of a problem, first with pain, then with mobility. The medication required to control the pain escalated rapidly to huge doses of narcotics. Assistance devices were required to get around: first a cane, then a walker, and finally a wheel chair. Nevertheless, Tim insisted on conducting church services. It was painful to watch him struggle up steep stairs to the high pulpit to deliver a sermon, obviously in pain. Fortunately, as Tim went through X-ray treatments and chemotherapy, two retired ministers took over many of his duties on a part-time basis.

The congregation mobilized to meet Tim's personal needs: food, laundry, dog walking, shopping, and so on. It was inspiring to see how church members rallied around their dying minister, especially since he had only been their minister for a few months.

Our lunches became a regular part of Tim's life and mine. And my responsibilities grew from providing lunch to filling other needs as well. I picked up laundry, transported Tim to wherever he needed to go: doctor's appointments, chemotherapy infusions, even shopping for a new cellphone or a small digital TV.

From time to time, I would discretely bring up issues that I thought Tim should take care of, such as having a will and an advance directive that spelled out his wishes for medical care in the event that he could not decide for himself. I also hinted at resolving any unmet emotional and spiritual issues, but I felt that was more Tim's area of expertise than mine.

I did share some stories of my patients who had near-death experiences that brought up the prospect of an afterlife. I was curious to know if Tim believed in an afterlife and, if so, if that belief brought him any comfort. Tim listened to my stories with interest but never pursued the implications. Similarly, when the subject of his illness came up unavoidably, he never seemed to want to discuss it. He just didn't want to face up to the expected course of his disease. Well into his illness, he told me: "I know I'm going to die. Everybody will. I'd like to have another 20 years, but if it is only five years, I'll just have to face that possibility when the time comes."

I winced. The time for realistic planning had already come and almost gone. He had been through three different courses of chemotherapy, none of which had helped. There had also been little benefit from X-ray treatments. Surgery had nothing to offer. It was the end of the road. Tim would be lucky to live five months, but he was only grudgingly accepting five years and still hoping for 20. Tim was in denial and beginning to bargain in psychiatrist Elisabeth Kübler-Ross's five stages of emotional response to a fatal illness: denial, anger, bargaining, depression and, finally, acceptance. I wished that Tim could leapfrog over the other responses and go directly to acceptance. Knowing that his death was not long off, I would have liked to see Tim more at peace with mortality. Still, I could easily understand how a 50-year-old man, one who had just started a ministry that he had long prepared for, could have trouble accepting his grim outlook.

Tim was not only in denial about his impending death; he was also in denial about his inability to carry on as our minister. We were his first church as the elected minister, and he already thought of the congregation as his new family and his personal responsibility. He wanted to remain on the job in Maine for years to come. But his birth family and his personal roots were primarily on the West Coast.

As the terminal phase of his illness approached, I worried that he would suddenly face some medical crisis that made him unable to travel back to end his life with the support of his family and longtime friends. Also, the church needed to start the lengthy search process for a new minister. It was time for Tim to go home, but going home meant facing up to the reality of his cancer and leaving the congregation that had supported him so generously and that he had grown to love. It was a hard thing for Tim to do.

After many painful conversations with many different people, Tim finally went back to the West Coast. He visited his ex-wife and her daughter and new grandchild. He spent a few days at his family's summer camp on an island in Puget Sound. And he spent three weeks with his father and stepmother in Sacramento.

Tim said his goodbyes and visited old haunts. He had finally found the courage and the will power to make the move before it was too late.

In California the disease progressed rapidly. The pain got worse. X-rays showed that the cancer had spread in an alarming way, including to his brain. One night, the pain became so bad that Tim was rushed to the hospital. He was in agony. A large dose of narcotics finally succeeded in quieting the pain and dispelling his anxiety. Tim went to sleep. His family was at the bedside.

He never woke up.

Tim taught me a lot about ministering to patients with a fatal illness. I had assumed that he would like to draw on my medical knowledge and particularly my experience with end-of-life care. But, especially at first, he did not want to talk about his disease at all, even to discuss how "to live as fully as possible for as long as possible," to borrow a hospice phrase. Tim simply wanted the support of a caring friend, someone who would simply be present with him, someone to listen, but only to what he wanted to talk about, not to bring up concerns that he was not ready to face.

In our wide-ranging conversations, I was greatly impressed by the breadth of Tim's knowledge. It was no accident that he had five academic degrees. Tim had an active and curious mind. He was a true scholar with a great deal of book knowledge about many fields. But books do not often bring comfort in a life-threatening crisis. Comfort is more apt to come from the love and support of family and friends. Or a strong religious faith. Tim needed faith and love to help him cope with the devastating prospect of an early death—and a ministry that he loved left undone.

CHAPTER 25

The Baptist Minister

—

Tim's early death reminded me of the early death of Mike Scroggin, a friend and a much-loved Baptist minister in Worcester. Like Tim, Mike Scroggin was a big man, about six feet three inches tall and 240 pounds, with more bone and muscle than fat. He had been a high-school football lineman, and he looked the part. However, he was a gentle giant, soft-spoken, and perhaps a bit shy.

Betty and I first met Mike when we moved to Worcester and were church-shopping. When we lived in the Boston area, we had attended a Unitarian church in Dedham, a suburb of Boston. After we moved, we attended the Unitarian church in Worcester. But we didn't like the service, so we looked around at other churches. Two or three people told us that we really ought to listen to a sermon by Mike Scroggin, the pastor of the First Baptist Church. Having grown up in Kentucky and Tennessee and having experienced Southern Baptist services there, I was skeptical. But the First Baptist Church in Worcester was an American Baptist congregation and much more liberal than the Southern Baptists. We decided to give Mike a try. We were glad we did.

Mike's sermons were, in large part, literary exercises. He was a voracious reader, and he managed to work whatever he had read recently into his sermons. He frequently included poems or readings from current novels. He didn't dwell much on Christian dogma, to my relief, and he drew inspiration from other religions as well, especially Judaism and Buddhism. He emphasized good works and a life of service to others. While never disavowing his Baptist roots, he seemed much broader and more universal in his own beliefs than other Baptist ministers I had known. He was well-known in the community, playing leadership roles in several charitable organizations, especially those dealing with young people. He was, in every sense of the word, a good man.

Because of Mike, we attended services regularly at the First Baptist Church, even though we never could bring ourselves to join the church formally. We were just not Baptists. However, we made an annual pledge of financial support and participated in church activities. One of our daughters was married in the church chapel by Mike. We regarded Mike as our minister, but we had limited personal contact. He was quite busy serving a large congregation and being active in the community. I was also quite busy. But he and his wife, Sue Ellen, did come to dinner at our home, and we saw them frequently at church. We regarded them as friends.

Sometimes I used to see Mike jogging on the streets near his home. Big man that he was, jogging looked like an effort. And one day it struck me that Mike was really struggling to make it up a hill. His steps were short and slow, and his face was red and sweaty. I wondered if something was wrong with Mike. It was, as soon became apparent.

Not long after I saw him jogging with such difficulty, Mike invited us to join him and Sue Ellen for a Sunday brunch at a local hotel. Once a year, he had the opportunity to invite a visiting speaker to do the homily at a Sunday service. The speakers were usually distinguished leaders in the forefront of some socially relevant cause. Often they were authors. The speaker whom Mike had invited for that particular year was Li-Young Li, an immigrant Chinese-American poet, whose poems he had read from the pulpit. After the Sunday service, Mike and Sue Ellen planned to take Li-Young Li to the Beechwood Hotel's Sunday brunch. They invited us to join them. We were delighted to do so.

The hotel's chef had prepared a lavish display of elegant food with many exotic dishes, strikingly presented. As always at an attractive buffet, I struggled to avoid overloading my plate—and did so anyway. But Mike's plate was almost bare, and what little food he took remained largely untouched. I remembered the pained expression on his face as he struggled to jog up the hill a few days before. I could not help but ask, "Mike, are you feeling all right?"

"To tell the truth, I have had a little stomach distress recently, but I'm seeing my doctor for it. I just don't feel like eating much at the moment."

"I'm sorry to hear that. I hope it gets better soon."

It was obviously not the time or place to probe for medical details, especially since he was seeing his own doctor. And something about Mike's manner didn't invite further questions. My attention turned to a lively conversation between Sue Ellen and Li-Young Li.

Li-Young Li had a fascinating personal history, basically one long flight from religious persecution in the Far East while he was growing up. His father was a Christian minister in China and Indonesia. Finally, the family found safety and opportunity through immigration to the United States. Mike listened attentively to Li-Young Li, but he seemed rather subdued. I wondered how badly his stomach was bothering him.

One afternoon, about two weeks later, I was busy working at my desk when my secretary buzzed me. She said, "Sue Ellen Scroggin is on the line. She says that she is a friend of yours and that it is very important for her to speak to you right now. Will you take the call?"

"Of course. Put her on the line." I had a sense of foreboding. Sue Ellen had never called me before.

Her voice was distraught. "Brownie, Mike has collapsed. I don't know what to do."

"Can you get him into the car safely?"

"I think so."

"Then get him into the car and drive straight to the ER. I will meet you there."

About ten minutes later, Sue Ellen's car pulled up in front of the ER entrance. Mike was slumped over in the passenger seat. I was waiting for them at the door. White-jacketed ER orderlies helped Mike onto a stretcher and wheeled him into an examining room. His initial medical history and physical examination did not point to any specific diagnosis, but laboratory tests showed an elevated blood calcium level—a finding that can be due to cancer involving the bones. Bone X-rays were obtained. When I saw them, my heart sank. Mike's bones were riddled with round black holes. Each hole indicated to me the presence of cancer cells that had eaten away the surrounding bone. The fragments of bone destroyed by the cancer had released calcium into the bloodstream, causing elevation in the level of blood calcium. Mike was in trouble ... bad, bad, bad trouble. He was admitted to the hospital for further diagnostic work-up and, hopefully, treatment.

Extensive tests revealed adenocarcinoma, a type of cancer that can originate in many sites, especially the stomach, colon, pancreas, and lung. Sometimes the primary site is never identified. There were some hints that Mike's cancer came from his stomach, but I was never convinced that we ever proved the original site. Perhaps it didn't matter. There is no good treatment for any of these cancers, once they have spread as widely as in Mike's case.

Once in the hospital, Mike seemed rather passive and detached. He was content to put himself in the hands of his doctors. He didn't question the diagnosis or the gloomy outlook. Sue Ellen, on the other hand, was understandably and appropriately aggressive about doing everything possible to save her 50-year-old husband. She wanted to fight this disease with every weapon available. A second opinion was sought and obtained in Boston. The consultant supported all the steps taken by our UMass medical team and offered nothing new in terms of treatment.

Mike seemed satisfied that no stone had been left unturned and resigned to accept whatever was in store for him. Sue Ellen, on the other hand, refused to regard Mike's illness as incurable. She clung to the hope that if he only fought hard enough, he could beat this cancer into submission by force of his own willpower. She stayed constantly by his bedside. She controlled who went in and out, ensuring as much rest for Mike as possible. No visitors were allowed, although many friends and church members were anxious to visit Mike and wish him a speedy recovery. But it was clearly not going to be a speedy recovery. Chemotherapy was started, but Mike was rapidly losing weight and strength. I felt that we were approaching the end.

I wondered if Mike was aware that that was the case and whether or not he was prepared in every way. At least I felt that he should know the full story. But in his hospital room, with Sue Ellen always by his side, I knew that there was to be no defeatist talk about death. One day, she implored me: "Brownie, you've got to make Mike fight! He's giving up. You've got to make him fight!"

I winced. I was all in favor of a positive and optimistic approach to medical care, wherever possible. And I think a patient's attitude can make a big difference. The mind can indeed influence the body. But I also knew that unrealistic hopes sometimes lead to lack of preparation for an inevitable outcome and result in unnecessary pain and suffering. I thought that Mike might be letting go in a realistic and appropriate way, considering his medical situation.

Not long after that, I paid a visit to Mike at a time when, to my surprise, Sue Ellen was not in the room. The two of us were alone. It was an opportunity to find out what Mike understood about his outlook and to help in any way that I could.

"Mike, are there any questions you would like to ask me about your medical situation? Or have all your questions been answered by your other doctors?"

He paused as though considering the question. "I know that I am dying." His tone was subdued, but not at all fearful or angry. Rather, there was a calm acceptance. A simple matter of fact.

I replied, "I guess we all are, sooner or later. But you may be on a faster track than the rest of us. Is there any way you can think of in which I can be helpful?"

"I don't think so, thanks. ... I'm not afraid to die." Again, a calm acceptance. Without a hint of anger or bitterness.

"You seem remarkably composed! What has gotten you through all this?"

"I believe that death is a natural part of life. ... And I don't believe that death is the end of life."

We talked for a few more minutes. Mike knew his situation and had made peace with it. His faith was firm, even in the face of his impending death. His words from the pulpit held up in his own life, despite the greatest of all challenges. I felt buoyed up, inspired. He said the best sermon I had ever heard. I felt almost as if I should take off my shoes, since the ground on which I stood in that sickroom had been made sacred by Mike's religious faith.

I walked out of the room feeling ten feet tall. Mike had no need of anything I could provide. With the help of whatever good angels Mike had, he was at peace, even knowing that his death was near.

Mike's hospital course was rapidly downhill from there. A few days later, the head nurse on Mike's ward called me to say that he had died, quietly and peacefully. I went to his room. Sue Ellen was sitting by his bedside. I was relieved to see that she looked surprisingly composed. In her heart, she must have known for weeks that this moment was coming. Mike's body was stretched out on the bed in his pajamas. His eyes were closed, and his face was unnaturally pale. It was the face of death. Instinctively, I put a hand on his ankle. His skin was cold to the touch. The flesh felt lifeless to me.

Sue Ellen told me that she would like to sit with Mike's body for a while longer before it was taken away to the hospital morgue. Whatever she wanted to do was fine with me, but it was also apparent to me that the animating spirit that was Mike was no longer in that cold, pale body. I wondered where that spirit was. Somehow I was sure that Mike was in a good place.

Some weeks later, the church held a memorial service appropriately called a service of thanksgiving for Mike's life. In his brief 50 years, Mike had touched the lives of many people in a positive way. The church probably seated 1,500 people, and it was packed to overflowing. A parade of clergy of all faiths marched down the center aisle onto the stage. They made glowing tributes to their colleague. The service was truly a celebration of a life well spent. A thanksgiving. I felt good about the service, despite the tragedy of a 50-year-old man dying in the prime of his life. I also took comfort in remembering my brief private conversation with Mike in the hospital. I knew that he had died at peace, ready for whatever came next.

CHAPTER 26

Playing Charades With Death

—

"Sandy" Sandberg was a remarkably talented man with three degrees from Harvard. A charitable foundation administrator, lawyer, and businessman, he was also a concert pianist with a sharp wit and a dry sense of humor. But despite his brilliance and general savvy, he was unable to protect himself from unwanted intensive care after complications from cancer surgery left him in a hopeless medical condition. With a breathing tube in his throat, unable to speak, Sandy invented a unique way to make his wishes known. It made me an accomplice in his death, although I was slow at first to grasp the high-stakes game we were playing.

Joan Sandberg, Sandy's wife, was a longtime friend of my wife Betty's. Their friendship dated back to grade school. Joan's childhood nickname was Nonnie, and that was what we always called her. Nonnie was a bridesmaid in Betty's wedding, and Betty was a bridesmaid in Nonnie's wedding.

Nonnie graduated from Smith College and moved to Manhattan. There she met Sandy. He was an adopted child. Wherever his genes originated, they were jam-packed with musical talent. Sandy was a concert-level pianist. In college he performed in the Sunday concert series at the Gardner Museum in Boston. He also performed concerts in many other venues, including one in South America in a hall seating 3,000 people. He wrote music, including satirical pop musicals.

Nonnie was an excellent pianist herself. Their living room had side-by-side Steinway concert grand pianos, where they enjoyed playing piano duets.

But Sandy's chosen career wasn't in music. He worked for the Ford Foundation, supervising philanthropic projects. For several years, he and Nonnie lived in Colombia where he worked on humanitarian projects.

Nonnie's father was the head of a successful family business involving both a steel plant and an oil storage business. He persuaded Sandy to leave the Ford Foundation and come to Portland, first to work in, and ultimately to head up, the family business. Sandy didn't particularly like the business world. But with his sharp mind, his law degree, and his broad past experience, he was quite successful. He satisfied his personal needs through his music. Ultimately, the business was sold, and Sandy retired. He looked forward to leaving business worries behind and having more time for his music.

About the time Sandy retired, I also retired. Betty and I moved to the Portland area, where Betty had grown up and she had relatives and longtime friends, especially Nonnie and Sandy. I looked forward to seeing more of them. I thought they might well become our best friends in retirement.

After we moved to Maine, we had dinner with Nonnie and Sandy in their home several times, and they came to our house for dinner as well. We reminisced, we listened to Sandy play the piano, and we talked about their interests and ours. Sandy was particularly interested in my post-retirement efforts to improve end-of-life care.

One evening at dinner, I thought that Sandy didn't look well. He had grown increasingly thick in the middle. He didn't do much exercise, except to walk his dog. He also didn't look healthy in subtle ways that I couldn't define very well, despite my years of clinical experience. It was a sort of medical intuition that I gradually acquired over many years of clinical practice. I noted something about the color of his skin, the expression on his face, the look of his eyes, the way he moved, and other subtle clues. At any rate, I wasn't too surprised when Nonnie told us one day that Sandy had cancer of the bladder, requiring major surgery.

With Sandy's permission, I talked to his urologist. She told me that Sandy's tumor was extensive and would require a radical operation involving removal of the entire bladder and surrounding tissues, followed by reconstruction of a new bladder from a loop of bowel. It all sounded quite worrisome, but also quite clear in its medical indications. And the urologist seemed well-trained and qualified to perform the procedure.

Several days later, after further testing and pre-operative preparation, the surgery was carried out. The surgeon told me that the cancer had proved too extensive to remove, but an artificial bladder had been constructed to prevent the tumor from obstructing the flow of urine. X-ray treatment and chemotherapy would be given when Sandy's condition permitted, but the tumor was a highly malignant type that typically didn't respond well to treatment. Sandy's outlook was for a few brief months of life at best. And the quality of his life would be greatly diminished by a rapidly growing cancer, as well as by aggressive attempts to slow the cancer's growth with toxic drugs and X-ray treatments—not to mention having his urine drain out into a bag glued to his abdomen.

Three or four days after the surgery, I went to see Sandy. He was propped up in bed and actually looked better than I had expected. The procedure had been less stressful than expected, since he never had the extensive dissection and the long operating time that I thought would be required. That was the good news, such as it was. The bad news was that his cancer was incurable.

Sandy had been told exactly what the surgeon found. He knew that the cancer had not been removed, and that X-ray treatment and perhaps chemotherapy were in store. But it hadn't really registered with him. He was simply glad to have surgery behind him. In his mind, the future was vague and undefined, still truly the future. Visiting him that day, I didn't dwell on the unpleasant realities. I was glad to see my friend looking somewhat relieved and not too uncomfortable. I did not realize that the next day would be the beginning of the end.

Cancer patients sometimes don't heal as quickly or as well as other patients, and their surgical wounds are not as strong. The next day, Sandy tried to cough up some phlegm and felt a sudden, sharp pain in the incision. A watery, salmon-pink discharge stained his dressing. It was abdominal fluid, stained with blood. Sandy had suffered what surgeons call a "dehiscence," which simply means that the surgical incision has pulled apart. When a dehiscence occurs, loops of bowel may extrude from the abdominal cavity unless restrained by a bulky pressure dressing. In such cases, it is nearly always best to re-suture the wound. But a dehiscence is a serious complication of surgery, even if re-sutured. A sick patient has to undergo another anesthesia and another operation. This often sets the stage for further complications.

Sandy was taken back to the operating room, and the wound was re-sutured. After surgery, he was taken to the intensive care unit because of deterioration in his lung function.

I won't go into all the details of his subsequent downhill course. I will simply say that a month later, Sandy was still in the ICU, a breathing tube in his throat and on a respirator. No visitors were allowed. A sign read "immediate family only." I asked Nonnie if I could help in any way. She didn't see how, when I first inquired. But a few days later, to my surprise, she called back to say that Sandy wanted to see me. The ICU physician in charge had given his permission for me to consult informally on Sandy.

At the ICU, with permission of the staff, I reviewed Sandy's now voluminous hospital record. The outlook was not good. I did not see how he could survive very long. And even if he did somehow recover from the surgery and went home, what did he have to look forward to then? He had an aggressive, incurable cancer. Chemotherapy and X-ray treatment were probably futile and would certainly cause unpleasant side effects. His quality of life would be terrible. It was with a heavy heart that I went in to see my friend.

Nonnie was sitting by the bed, the head of which was raised to about a 30-degree angle. Sandy was propped up with a pillow, his cheeks sunken and pale. However, his eyes were restless and bright, his mind obviously alert. A breathing tube was taped to his cheek.

It was obvious that he could not talk, but that he wanted to communicate. I thought that he seemed glad to see me.

I had hardly entered the room when he stared intently into my eyes, almost seeming to say, "Now pay attention to this." With great emphasis, he pointed his index finger directly at me, then pointed his finger at himself, closed his eyes, and crossed his hands on his chest, lying quietly and peacefully in that posture for a few seconds. All I could think of was the medieval statues resting on top of tombs in European cathedrals. Sandy's movements seemed quite deliberate, almost rehearsed. He looked at me as much as to say, "Did you get it?" For my part, this was all totally unexpected. I wasn't at all sure what was going on.

"Sandy, are you trying to tell me something?"

He nodded affirmatively. Once again, slowly and with great emphasis, he pointed first to me, then to himself, then closed his eyes and crossed his hands on his chest in the posture of a dead medieval knight at peace in his cathedral tomb.

Slowly, dimly, I perceived that Sandy was playing a life-and-death game of charades with me. I recalled his interest in my postretirement efforts to improve end-of-life care. We had even talked about the futility of overly aggressive care in dying patients. It all began to fall together.

Slowly, I said, "I think I get it, Sandy. But I want to be sure. Tell me again."

With a relieved but slightly exasperated look, Sandy repeated the now familiar routine one more time. I was sure that I was not mistaken in the meaning of this grim and silent game of charades, with Sandy's fate hanging in the balance. He was saying, "Please, help me die in peace." The question now was whether Nonnie understood and interpreted it all in the same way I did.

"I get what you're trying to tell me, Sandy. I think that Nonnie and I should have a cup of coffee now and come back later."

He seemed satisfied.

We left for the Maine Medical Center cafeteria. It was about 11am. Too late for breakfast, too early for lunch. The large institutional dining room was deserted, except for a few employees taking a late coffee break. Nonnie and I each got a cup of coffee at the counter and sat down at a far corner of the room, well out of earshot of other people.

I asked, "Well, what did you make of all that?"

Nonnie leaned toward me and looked earnestly into my eyes. There was a brief pause, as she considered the seriousness of what she was about to say. "I think … he wants to die," she finally said.

There was no doubt in her voice. She had witnessed the same desperate plea that I had. She had been struck equally by the force and urgency of Sandy's manner.

"Does Sandy have a health-care proxy?" I asked.

Yes, he did. It turned out that Nonnie was his legal health-care agent. She could ask that only comfort measures, including pain relief, be used in his care. She could ask that more aggressive treatment be stopped, including the distress of the breathing tube, even if it might lead to his death.

I told her that quite honestly, as an experienced surgeon, I saw no reasonable hope that Sandy would survive his severe complications and be discharged from the hospital. I also said that no doctor was infallible and no prediction was 100 percent accurate. I added that even though Sandy clearly wanted to die and be spared further suffering, if through some miracle he did survive, at a later date he might be quite grateful that his caregivers had persisted in heroic efforts to save his life.

Nonnie took all of this in without comment. Obviously, she, like Sandy, had been thinking through his distressing situation and considering all possible outcomes. Nothing I said came as a surprise.

After a pause, she said, "But even if he survives now, he'll still have the cancer,"

It was true, of course. And the cancer was a bad one with its own distressing complications, its predictably poor response to any type of treatment, and its short life expectancy. Sandy might well want to die, simply to escape what lay before him, even if the palliative surgery had an uneventful recovery.

I asked, "Considering the whole picture, what do you think Sandy would want us to do?" After a discussion of all options, we agreed that he would want to be taken off the breathing tube and the respirator, even knowing (perhaps hoping) that it might lead to his early death. He would then be able to talk to people and to tell them exactly what his wishes were. We assumed that he would insist on only getting treatment to relieve pain and provide comfort. Nonnie would support Sandy's wishes if his physicians objected.

(*The story from here on is what Nonnie told me later. I wasn't present for these events.*)

When she went back to the ICU, Sandy seemed

to understand and agree with what we had concluded, although he couldn't speak for himself with the breathing tube in his throat. Nonnie then talked to her son and to the head doctor in the ICU. But the doctor did not want to remove the endotracheal tube, saying that it might prove fatal and that Sandy might yet be found to have some treatable condition that could allow him to recover. He suggested that another CT scan of the abdomen be done, hoping to detect an abscess that might be drained with improvement in Sandy's condition. Despite some reluctance, Nonnie gave permission for the CT scan.

Though it was a problem to transport a critically ill patient on a respirator to the X-ray department and carry out a CT scan of the abdomen, the medical staff managed to do so. They discovered nothing new or treatable, but everyone seemed relieved to think that no stone had been left unturned. And the ICU physician gave his permission to remove the breathing tube and institute comfort measures only.

Sandy was very weak, but he seemed greatly relieved to be able to speak again. He took the opportunity to make three last requests.

The first was that he could see his Labrador retriever, his faithful companion at home and on walks. To the great credit of the compassionate ICU staff, they broadened the definition of "immediate family" to include a golden-haired Labrador retriever.

The second request was a shock to Nonnie: Sandy wanted to see a priest. Nonnie knew that he had been raised in the Roman Catholic faith; but as long as she had known Sandy, he had never professed any religious beliefs and never attended Mass. Still, knowing his life was drawing to a close, Sandy wanted to talk to a priest. The visit was arranged. What was said was private, but whatever it was, it seemed to comfort Sandy.

The last request was to have his son, Bill, read some of Sandy's favorite poems and readings to him. After listening to some of these old favorites, Sandy picked out one or two for Bill to read at the memorial service that both knew would not be long in coming.

After his three requests had been granted, Sandy seemed at peace, even if his breathing was labored. The next day he closed his eyes and gradually became less responsive. Sometimes his breath would stop for a few moments, but then resume. The periods without breathing became longer. It all seemed natural, peaceful. At last, his breathing simply stopped.

Sandy had his wish.

But it should not have been so hard! With his intelligence and his legal background, Sandy should have been able to make his wishes clear much sooner. He should have been able to spare himself nearly a month of futile suffering. Ironically, he had actually filled out documents giving his wife the health-care power of attorney to act for him. But he had not engaged her in a meaningful discussion of his wishes. Who welcomes having such a conversation? Still, legal forms are often useless if the family hasn't had a full and frank discussion with the patient about wishes for end-of-life care. And few patients on a respirator can play charades to make their wishes known. Fortunately, Sandy was able to invent a wordless game that spared him more futile suffering.

The rest of us should be sure to have a frank discussion of our wishes for end-of-life care with our loved ones before the crisis. It is not enough to simply fill out the appropriate paperwork. Family members who have not been in such a conversation may object to withholding life support, despite documents that show that was the patient's wish. They protest: *I cannot believe that my mother would not want everything possible done to prolong her life!* In the heat of a health-care crisis, it is hard to change their minds. So, aggressive life support is used contrary to the patient's wishes. Sandy had gone a long way down that life-support road, but he was able to change direction by a clever pantomime. Few people would have had the imagination to convey their wishes in that way.

CHAPTER 27

When the Mind Dies

—

"Don't ever let this happen to me!" My mother-in-law was emphatic. Betty and I were in her living room, talking about the Old Ladies' Home in Portland, Maine. She was a member of their board of trustees, and she was quite concerned about the fate of poor and mentally incompetent women, especially those with no family to care for them. The Old Ladies' Home could care for a few indigent women, but the need was far greater than the home could meet. Many of the women who lived there were totally out of touch with reality. They no longer recognized family or friends. They could not dress themselves. Some could not even feed themselves. Their situation was a tragic and humiliating way to end their lives. Dying under such conditions was what my mother-in-law wanted to ensure never happened to her. She was asking for our help to avoid that fate. And a few years later, we failed her, despite our best intentions.

My mother-in-law, Florence Maxwell, was probably in her sixties when she made this plea. She was healthy and mentally alert. It was hard to imagine her ever becoming demented and dependent on others for her most basic needs. So we ignored her depressing statement and shifted the conversation to something more cheerful. Looking back many years later, I see that request was the moment when we should have had a long family discussion to fully understand her wishes and document them in writing. But like most people, we didn't want to talk about death or, worse yet, dementia in our own family. So we set the stage for a decade of totally dependent nursing home care in which she didn't recognize her own family members. My mother-in-law would have been horrified and humiliated if she could have foreseen how she would end her life.

The onset was insidious. After her husband's death, Florence decided, quite reasonably, to move out of their big house and into a smaller one-floor house in a new condo development. It was designed for easy living— pleasant and attractive and convenient. The owners' association managed the grounds and plowed the sidewalks. Help was available if needed. It seemed ideal for a retired couple or a widow, but Florence was never happy there.

We had trouble pinning down just why she was unhappy. Although she was 81 years old, she had no specific complaints, apart from feeling lonely. She just seemed to have trouble coping with the little demands of everyday life. She also became increasingly forgetful. I suspect that she was aware of her declining competency and depressed by it. What she complained of, though, was her isolation in her new home.

Florence wanted to move into Portland House, a new ten-story apartment building on the Eastern Promenade with views of Portland Harbor. Some of the tenants had been her friends. She was convinced that she would be happier living there. So the change was made.

In her new apartment, life was no better. In fact, her lack of familiarity with her new surroundings seemed to make things worse. Her forgetfulness got worse, and she had periods of confusion. Before long, we realized she would have to go to a nursing home. After a search of all available options, she was admitted to a double room at St. Joseph's Home. The staff seemed caring and committed to the welfare of their patients. The common rooms were spacious, light, and airy. The clientele, however, seemed depressing to me. Many were strapped in wheelchairs, often parked in front of a TV screen that they were oblivious to. We wondered how Florence would react to her new environs.

As nearly as I could tell, she reacted by withdrawing from the world. In what seemed like a short time, she was sitting in a wheelchair with the other residents in front of a television she had no interest in watching. After a few months had passed, she no longer seemed to know her own family. My wife felt compelled from time to time to visit her mother, a 150-mile trip in each direction. She would return frustrated, not knowing whether or not her mother knew she was there.

The nursing care was good, though. The nursing staff was caring and kind to the home's residents. The only real complaint we ever had was one time when we found her diamond engagement ring had been taken off her finger and was missing. I doubt if she ever knew what happened. The nursing supervisor was horrified and assured us that no one on her staff would ever dream of stealing a ring from a patient. Perhaps she was right, but someone took the ring.

Florence's mind was gone. It was merciful that she was not able to be aware of her situation. She was a proud, dignified lady, who would have been humiliated to see what her life had become. She would certainly have hoped that some friendly illness would carry her off and spare her and her family from her dementia.

Weeks turned into months, and months turned into years. When would it end? Once when we were visiting, I asked the nurse on duty, How is Mrs. Maxwell doing?

"Oh, she's so much better!"

"In what way? How is she better?"

"Well, a couple of days ago, she had a fever and a cough. She looked quite sick. We were afraid we might lose her, but we got right on it. We called Dr. Webber and he ordered some antibiotics. Within 24 hours, she was much better."

Inwardly, I groaned. *Pneumonia*, I thought. When frail, elderly patients are near death, they often don't have the strength to cough up any phlegm in their chest. A few opportunistic germs can grow in those secretions, and pneumonia can develop. With little resistance to infection, it can progress rapidly, even to the death of the patient. It is often a relatively peaceful way to die, much better than many others, which is why old-time practitioners once referred to pneumonia as the "old man's friend." But Florence had missed her chance. Her nurses had been too alert, and the antibiotics had been too effective for Florence to die peacefully. It was sad, since that would have been her most fervent wish. She would never have wanted her body to live on without her mind.

As far as I was concerned, the Florence Maxwell that I had known and loved had died some years back. Keeping her body alive when her mind was gone seemed wrong to me. My wife and her brothers agreed. We had already put a "do not resuscitate" order in effect. Now, after talking to her physician, an order was placed to withhold antibiotics unless they were administered for her comfort. We had not thought to take that step earlier.

Florence lived two more years, nearly a decade in the nursing home, not knowing her family or understanding where she was during that whole time. It was pointless. To me, it seemed strange and unnatural to keep someone alive who showed no sign of being able to think. It was also expensive. Medicare, Social Security, supplementary private insurance, and family funds each paid many thousands of dollars. I wished that some of that money had been available for poor families for prenatal care, childhood immunizations, and preventive health-care or other medical care our country does not provide for everyone. Still, I respected the caring nursing staff to whom it would have been unthinkable not to feed someone who would die otherwise.

Many times my wife, Betty, and I discussed the ethics of feeding her mother. We made sure that each of us understood thoroughly that the other never wanted to be fed under similar circumstances. We also had our lawyer put the appropriate language in our health-care proxies. We discussed it with our children. We continue to feel sad that Florence lived roughly ten years after her consciousness had deserted her. It was just the sort of living death that she had asked us never to let happen to her. She did not know how to prevent it. Unfortunately, at that time, neither did we.

The family struggle with dementia did not end with Florence. Ten years after her death, her son Richard began to be more forgetful than seemed usual for an older person. Richard was in his early seventies at the time. At first, we didn't think too much about it. Lots of senior citizens complain of being forgetful. But other warning signs began to appear too. For example, one lovely summer day there was a family reunion at his younger brother Bill's vacation home in the Belgrade Lakes of Maine. Richard had learned canoeing as a child at summer camp, and he had done a lot of canoeing over the years. I regarded him as an expert paddler. So I asked him if he would like to join me in a canoe trip around the lake. I also asked him if he would like to paddle in the stern. The stern paddler has better control of direction and generally is the more experienced canoeist. The stern paddler is in charge, and it is more fun to paddle stern. I thought that I was not only deferring to Richard's experience, but also offering him the choice seat. So we set off with Richard in the stern.

We hadn't gone far before I realized that something was terribly wrong. The canoe would start on a course to the left and then suddenly veer to the right. More worrisome, it would tip first to one side, then the other, as Richard shifted his weight unpredictably, sometimes adding his weight to mine on the same side of the canoe. (One of the cardinal rules of canoeing is to paddle on opposite sides in order to balance the weight. If one partner needs to shift sides, he tells the other so that both shift their weight at the same time and keep the canoe balanced.) With our combined weight suddenly on the same side of the canoe without any prior warning, I was afraid that the canoe might roll over in the middle of the lake. What in the world was going on?

I turned around to look at Richard. He looked

confused. I realized with a shock that Richard no longer knew how to handle a canoe. I knew that we had to get back to the dock as soon as we could, before we turned the canoe over.

So I asked Richard to let me do all the paddling. He seemed relieved to let me. And so we went back. Managing the canoe from the bow seat is a bit awkward. It involves shifting the paddle from one side to the other, but I was relieved to be in charge. I was shocked at how confused Richard had been. It was my first inkling that Richard's mental problems were much more serious than simply being forgetful.

Richard's wife and children knew long before I did that he was beginning to lose his ability to think clearly. He was seen by medical specialists and referred to a clinic at Yale-New Haven Medical Center that specializes in Alzheimer's disease. Many tests were done. Various medications were prescribed. Nothing seemed to help much. Periods of confusion became more frequent and more severe. His wife became afraid to leave him alone in the house. His two sons had to drive roughly an hour each way to take turns mowing the grass and doing any other household chores that Richard used to do and that his wife was unable to do. It was a burden on everyone, including Richard, who was well aware of the progressive decline in his mental capabilities.

Richard must have thought of his mother's last days many times. It must have been unbearably depressing. Who would want to end his life that way? On one occasion, walking the beach with his brother Bill, he said sadly, *I should take a long walk, off a short pier.* His meaning was clear: He would prefer to commit suicide by drowning himself rather than die in the way his mother had.

But he didn't commit suicide. Before long, his mental condition deteriorated to the point that he would not have been able to jump off a pier and drown himself or to commit suicide in any other way that required thought and effort. However, a subtle way of ending his life still remained. He could stop eating. Whether or not he knew this consciously or instinctively was never clear, but for whatever reason, he began to resist efforts to feed him.

He had been admitted to a nursing home when caring for him at home simply became too much for his wife. The nursing home staff was kind and caring, and the nursing home physician was also Richard's primary care doctor. Still, Richard would not eat. He lost weight, slept more and more, and finally became difficult to arouse. He was transferred to a nearby hospital, where they found that he was quite dehydrated and malnourished. He was resuscitated rather easily by intravenous fluids and transferred back to the nursing home. But he still resisted efforts to feed him. An attempt was made to pass a plastic tube through his nose into his stomach in order to feed him. He fought off the tube.

Richard's family held a meeting about what to do. Richard's mental condition had gotten steadily worse. There was no longer any hope of recovery. Everyone agreed that he would never have wanted to live like this. Nor would he have agreed to a surgical procedure to place a feeding tube through his abdominal wall. Having lost his ability to think, and having become a burden to those he loved, Richard would have wanted to die in peace with his loved ones nearby. And that is what happened. He did not eat or drink. After three or four days, he lapsed into a coma and died peacefully in the presence of his family. It was a blessing.

I can't say whether or not Richard willed his death through fasting and fluid restriction. Even if he had had the mental capacity to tell me, I doubt that he would have done so. But if he had asked my advice, I would have told him that fasting was a much better way to leave this world than jumping off a pier. All I know is that things worked out as he would have wished. Richard's fight with Alzheimer's disease is replicated in many homes across America. Many elderly people struggle with dementia. My own parents were not spared the loss of their mental ability late in life. My father tried his best to stay active, physically and mentally, as long as he could. He tended a vegetable garden lovingly into his nineties, and he did creative writing all that time as well. However, the time came that he needed help in dressing himself, taking a bath, and other activities of daily living. He was a heavy man, and my mother was not physically up to the job. And so he was admitted first to an assisted-living facility and later to a nursing home. As others took over his care, he rapidly lost what little ability he had left to care for himself. He seemed to have entered a world of his own, a world that we could never enter. He did not seem to know his caretakers. After a while, he did not know his family either.

One visit, I brought a copy of Robert Frost's poems. My father had always liked Frost, and I read some of his favorite poems out loud. He made no obvious response. However, the book included photographs of old New England farms taken by my friend Tony King, a gifted and sensitive photographer. The pictures of old farmhouses, barns, fields, forests, and farm animals were reminiscent of the old Wheeler family farm in eastern Kentucky. He looked at some of those pictures for a long time. I wondered if he remembered his boyhood on the farm. Perhaps that was now his world.

Unlike Richard, my father did not mind being fed. In fact, he seemed to enjoy his favorite foods. There were no decisions to be made about end-of-life care. We wondered how long he would live. It seemed it would be a long time. One night, though, the nurse making rounds simply found him, unexpectedly, dead in bed. There had been no prior warning of any change in his health. He was 97 years old. It was a kind and peaceful, and perhaps a bit overdue, way to go.

My mother never made it to a nursing home. Thank goodness! She was a proud woman, well aware of her appearance, and she would have been humiliated to be in my father's condition. Still, her mind had begun to slip, and she knew it. She had begun to have difficulty in shopping or in ordering from a restaurant menu. Counting out change was a challenge. She forgot things and sometimes repeated things that she had said before. But she could still dress herself attractively and carry on an enjoyable conversation. I hoped that she had some good years left.

I visited my mother shortly after my father had been admitted to the nursing home. Now that she was free of the responsibility to look after him, I hoped that she would be able to socialize more and do activities that she enjoyed. We went to a restaurant for lunch to talk about her new life. She studied the menu, had trouble deciding what to order, and finally told the waitress that she would have just what I had already ordered. After our food arrived, I said that I hoped she would enjoy her life more now that she did not have to look after my father. To my surprise, she said that the time had come for her to die. I protested, but she persisted.

"It's only natural, Brownell. I'm nearly 92 years old. Most of my best friends are dead. Some died a long time ago. I have had a long life—and a good life. I am ready to go anytime. It would be only natural."

She was speaking in a matter-of-fact way. There was no obvious emotion behind her words. No fear. No apprehension. No resignation. Just a statement of fact. Now that my father was cared for, she felt free to check out of this life with no regrets. Furthermore, she felt that it was only natural for her to do so. Her long life was surely drawing to its close.

I dropped the subject and enjoyed the rest of my visit. Just one week later, back home in Massachusetts, I got an urgent phone call from my brother in Nashville. My mother had suffered a serious heart attack. Four days later, she died, having refused to be placed on a mechanical ventilator. It almost seemed to me that she had willed her own death. Now she would never have to endure the worst indignities of old age. Above all, she would never lose her mind. She would never be admitted to a nursing home. She would never be dependent on the kindness of strangers to meet her every need. I was grateful that she would be spared the indignities so common in the very old—and that would have been so painful to my mother.

It is a terrible thing to lose your mind! And prevention is better than attempts to cure. Good health habits reduce the chances of losing your mind: regular physical and mental exercise, good nutrition, sleep, rest, nutritional supplements, and prescription drugs as indicated medically. An old adage applies to the mind, as well as the body: Use it or lose it!

But what if your best efforts at prevention fail? How do you avoid a long life in a nursing home, devoid of all reason, staring blankly at a television set, and failing to know your family when they come to visit? Again, prevention is the best insurance. Tell all your family what your wishes are, if your mind starts to go. Do you want to be resuscitated by life-support measures then if there is some health crisis? Do you want to be fed if you can't feed yourself? Do you want to be given powerful medications, including antibiotics, or just given medications that provide comfort? Your family should thoroughly understand your wishes. They should also be documented in an advance care directive, readily available to physicians and hospitals.

CHAPTER 28

The Trappist Monk

—

Father Raphael was a Trappist monk I knew at St. Joseph's Abbey in Spencer, Massachusetts. The monastery is known best for the fruit jams that support its work. Father Raphael had no fear at all of death. His strong Catholic faith led him to look forward to death and even to pray that it might come soon, God willing.

As a young man, Father Raphael had been a Jewish psychiatrist. He had been a student at the University of Chicago when President Robert Maynard Hutchins and the philosopher Mortimer Adler had revised the curriculum. They based their new curriculum on the "One Hundred Great Books" of Western civilization. The intellectual fervor of the program stimulated the entire university, including the graduate schools.

Adler was particularly impressed by the philosophy of Aristotle, and he passed that enthusiasm on to a young medical student, Kenneth Alwyn Simon, who spent a year in Berlin studying Aristotelian philosophy. Simon was from a Reformed Jewish family background. The study of Aristotle led him to study later philosophers who expanded on Aristotle's precepts. Prominent among them was St. Thomas Aquinas, who developed the philosophic foundations of the Roman Catholic Church. The young Dr. Simon was totally convinced by the philosophy of St. Thomas. Despite his Jewish heritage, he converted to Catholicism. He also left his medical career, became an ordained priest and, ultimately, a cloistered monk known as Father Raphael. Thus he began many decades of prayer and meditation and scholarly study in a Trappist monastery.

I met Father Raphael through Dr. John Meyers, a mutual friend and a prominent Jewish physician who had converted to Catholicism under the influence of Father Raphael. Neither of them felt that they had deserted the Jewish faith. Instead, they believed that Jesus was the long-awaited Jewish messiah and that Christianity was the logical culmination of Judaism.

Father Raphael was an important figure in Jack Meyers' life, and Jack frequently spoke to me about Father Raphael. I was curious as to just what had made a Jewish psychiatrist become a Catholic monk. Jack offered to arrange a meeting. This proved impossible for about three years because the new abbot had decreed that the monks were to remain in isolation during that time. Finally, the ban on visitors was lifted, and our visit was scheduled at the guesthouse at St. Joseph's Abbey.

I looked forward to finally meeting Father Raphael. I had never had the chance to talk to a cloistered monk. It almost seemed like talking to someone from another planet.

The appointed time arrived. Jack Meyers and I waited for Father Raphael in the lobby of the guesthouse. Soon he appeared, walking briskly. Father Raphael was an imposing figure: tall, large-framed, and military straight in posture. He wore the flowing, long, grey robes of his order. A black rosary was swinging at his waist as he walked. His hair was gray-white, and his dark eyes were piercing behind his steel-rimmed eyeglasses. His face had a kindly expression, but also one of great strength and inner conviction. He had a formidable presence, but not a threatening one. He wore large hearing aids, alerting me to the need to speak up and enunciate clearly.

Father Raphael ushered us into a sitting room and pulled his chair up close to mine, perhaps to hear better. I was full of curiosity about his background and what it was like to be a monk and live in a cloistered community. He answered freely, but asked me questions too, seeming much more interested in what it was like to be a surgeon and work in a medical school. He was relaxed, and he made me feel relaxed. I enjoyed getting to know him, and he seemed to enjoy getting to know me. I was surprised at how up-to-date he was about medicine, politics, and what was going on in the outside world. I was also surprised at how understandable he made life as a monk seem to be, although starting the day with prayer and meditation at 3:30 a.m. seemed a bit too Spartan for me.

That was the first of several widely spaced visits to Father Raphael. After Jack Meyers died of cancer, I continued to visit Father Raphael. We talked about Jack and about death. He was totally at peace with death. In fact, he looked forward to it. I enjoyed our occasional visits as the years went by and I looked forward to Father Raphael's dependable Christmas card, usually with a brief personal note. Late in life, he developed colorectal cancer that spread to his lungs. He welcomed it. I have kept his last Christmas card, which had this note attached, in his own handwriting:

May this Christmas bring you closer to Jesus,

Whom I hope to see in four months or a year, through His mercy.

My invitation to ascend higher is cancer, which is spreading.

You are on the list to be notified when I enter upon this wonderful adventure.

Love, Father Raphael

He died peacefully a few months later. I hope that his adventure was indeed as wonderful as he anticipated. Father Raphael was so confident that it was hard for me not to be confident too, even though I never could bring myself to share all of his other Catholic convictions.

His printed obituary at St. Joseph's Abbey concludes with his own words, written years earlier:

To fall in love with God is the greatest of all romances;
to seek him, the greatest adventure;
to find him, the greatest human achievement.

What more can I say about Father Raphael? Or his chosen way of life? He certainly found spiritual comfort that lasted right up to his death. I wish that were true of everyone.

Not surprisingly, ministers, priests, and rabbis are like other people with a wide spectrum of spiritual strengths and weaknesses. Some ministers are wise counselors; others are not. Some are spiritually enlightened; others are not. Some can provide guidance and comfort when you need it; others need it themselves. If your minister or priest or rabbi is an inspiring guide at a difficult time, you are fortunate.

CHAPTER 29

The Past Life Therapist

—

In January 1996, I retired after 25 years as chairman of surgery at UMass Medical Center. My successor was scheduled to start on Feb. 1. It seemed like a good time to take a midwinter vacation. The new chief could take over the department without feeling that the old chief was looking over his shoulder. I decided to take Betty snorkeling in warm Caribbean waters.

We had received a flyer from the Omega Institute in Rhinebeck, New York, advertising a two-week program at the Maho Bay Campground on St. John, U.S. Virgin Islands. This beautiful campground had platform tents in a hillside tropical forest, overlooking a lovely Caribbean beach. Meeting places had stunning views of the blue-green Caribbean, dotted with mountainous, dark green, volcanic islands. It was a good spot to get away, leaving behind the snow and ice of a New England winter for sun and sand on a beach. Little did I ever guess that it would also be my introduction to past-life therapy.

The Omega list of courses looked interesting too. Of greatest interest to us, Jon Kabat-Zinn, our good friend and fellow faculty member at UMass, was giving a shortened version of the mindfulness-based stress reduction program that he had developed at UMass Medical Center and that had subsequently been widely adopted elsewhere. Betty was also interested in a yoga program led by Beryl and Thom Birch. However, we expected to spend much of our time on the beach, snorkeling, reading, and relaxing. St. John, a relatively small island and mostly in a national park, did not have a commercial airport. To get there, we had to fly to nearby St. Thomas and take a ferry to Cruz Bay, the largest town on St. John. At Cruz Bay, a truck met us to take us to the campground. Plain board seats on each side of the truck bed accommodated about 12 of us campers and our luggage.

On the ride, I felt like we were sharing an adventure with a group that was sure to include some future friends. The ride encouraged informality and getting to know your neighbor.

Seated directly across from me was an intelligent-looking man, perhaps 50 years old with graying dark hair and metal-rimmed glasses. He was medium in height and slender in build. He had a somewhat professorial look about him. Despite his short-sleeved sport shirt and chino pants, I thought he would look right in place at a medical school faculty meeting.

"I'm Brownie Wheeler, and I live in Worcester, Massachusetts. Could I ask your name?"

"Nice to meet you, Brownie. I'm Brian Weiss, and I live in Miami."

The name meant nothing to me. And I had never much liked Miami.

"Nice to meet you too, Brian. I assume you are going to the Omega conference?"

"I'm one of the instructors."

For some reason, perhaps feeling a bit too intrusive with someone I had just met for the first time, I didn't pick up on his comment. It would have been a logical time to ask about his course. Instead, I reverted to cocktail party conversation. We talked about the pleasant weather, about St. John, about Maho Bay and so on. Before long, we were on the narrow, winding road to the campground and an open truck was not conducive to conversation.

That night we attended a welcoming reception with introductions to instructors of the various courses. They each described their own background and what they expected to cover in their courses. Brian Weiss said that he was originally from New York City and went to Columbia University. He then received his medical training at Yale, including a psychiatric residency and fellowship. After holding faculty positions at Yale and Pittsburgh universities, he had become the chief of psychiatry at Mount Sinai Hospital in Miami. His professional background and demeanor impressed me. I thought again that Brian Weiss would fit right in at one of our medical faculty meetings. So I was particularly surprised he said his course was Past-Life Therapy, a topic that I could never imagine on the agenda of a medical faculty meeting at Harvard or UMass. Interesting, I thought, an Ivy League-trained psychiatrist who is delving into some far-out field of psychology that challenges my view of reality. I decided to audit his course, at least once, and see what this interesting man had to say.

In the first meeting, Brian explained how he had stumbled into past-life therapy. His psychiatric training and early years of clinical practice had been fairly conventional with one exception: He had a particular interest and expertise in using hypnosis to uncover long-buried trauma, such as early childhood abuse. One day in Miami, his career veered in an entirely unforeseen direction when a young woman named Catherine came to him for relief of panic attacks. She did not respond to counseling, so he decided to try hypnosis. His usual introductory question, once the patient was hypnotized, had been something along these lines: Take yourself back to early childhood. See if that is when your trouble started. Sometimes that suggestion led to a description of physical or sexual abuse in early childhood and became the focus of future treatment. Follow-up questions under hypnosis often brought back long-repressed memories.

In treating Catherine, the young woman suffering from panic attacks, Brian Weiss unintentionally changed the wording of his introductory question: *Take yourself back to when your trouble first started*. After a pause, the patient described a deeply traumatic event. But it did not occur in her childhood. It occurred 4,000 years ago. It was an ancient memory of drowning in a flood in ancient Egypt while trying to save her baby.

Brian Weiss had no idea what to make of her story. However, the patient felt greatly relieved after dredging up this tragic "memory" from the depths of her psyche. Whatever the underlying explanation, the session under hypnosis was good treatment. A few more sessions under hypnosis revealed further details of past lives. Before long, the young woman was cured of her panic attacks. Brian Weiss was pleased with the outcome, but puzzled by the reason. He did not discuss this unusual case of "past-life therapy" with his colleagues. He did not change his usual approach to psychiatric practice.

As time went by, he saw other patients who, like

Catherine, were not helped by his usual therapeutic techniques. After all other treatment had failed, he tried hypnotic regression back in time to "when this trouble first started." In some patients, this led to dramatic tales of emotional trauma in a life they had lived in an earlier time and often in a far-off place. As with Catherine, dredging up stories of past lives helped to control the patient's present symptoms. Cautiously, Weiss began to ask some of his colleagues if they had ever had similar experiences. A few psychiatrists said that they had also seen patients with "past-life recall" under hypnosis. Weiss was intrigued. He had never believed in reincarnation, but now he went to the library to find out more about the history of this strange idea. He was surprised by what he found.

He started with his own religion, Judaism. Many Jews in earlier times had believed in reincarnation. The same was true of early Christians, as well as Buddhists and Hindus, who still believe in reincarnation. Many primitive cultures believe in reincarnation. And there have been many prominent people in Western civilization who have had experiences that convinced them of their own past lives. In short, Weiss was surprised at the widespread belief in reincarnation in many times and places, including Western civilization before the so-called "Enlightenment" of three centuries ago.

Brian's wife, Carol, urged him to report his clinical experiences to his colleagues. She felt that if past-life therapy was so useful to some patients, he was obligated to share the information, even at the risk of losing credibility with some of his skeptical colleagues. Reluctantly, he agreed.

He described Catherine's story in a book written for the lay public. Its title was *Many Lives, Many Masters*, and it sold two million copies. It was translated into 20 languages. Brian Weiss and past-life therapy were on the map to stay. Audiences flocked to attend his lectures, and patients came from surprising distances to seek treatment.

After explaining his own inadvertent introduction to past-life therapy, Brian Weiss had the group, perhaps 30 people, stretch out on the floor for an exercise in guided self-hypnotic suggestion. He told us to close our eyes, consciously relax our muscles, and observe our breathing. After we were thoroughly relaxed, he asked us to imagine that we were at the top of a long flight of stairs. Slowly, he counted down from 20 to one. With each number, we were to take a step down. Each step down took us back in time. At the bottom of the stairs was a lovely garden, he said, with a bench, where we should sit down and rest a few moments. At the far end of the garden was a door. When we opened the door, he told us, we would find ourselves in a past life. We were to let the images take shape in our minds without any attempt to judge or analyze or create them.

Once we imagined passing through the door, Brian's soft voice told us to look around. Where are you? ... Look at your feet. ... What is your footwear like? ... Look at your hands. ... Are they the rough hands of a worker? ... Or the dainty hands of a lady ... What clothes are you wearing? ...What are you doing? ... Brian's faint voice told us just to let the images come spontaneously, not to force them.

Lying there with my eyes closed, deeply relaxed, I

wondered dreamily what I might see. At first, my mind was empty, but slowly an image took place. I was in a large room with a tall, slitlike window through which I could see rugged mountains with snowy peaks in the background. Curiously, there were no glass panes in the window. The room seemed to be in the upper stories of an ancient castle or monastery. I was wearing sandals and a robe. I was amused to watch ten or 12 young boys, wearing similar robes and sandals, running around on a field some distance below my window. They were playing a game that resembled "Tag! You're It!" I knew that I was an old man and that I was the boys' teacher. I liked my life as a teacher, and I was fond of the young boys who were my pupils. With a start, I realized that one of the boys reminded me of my friend Jon Kabat-Zinn.

Brian's quiet voice broke into my reverie. Slowly, he had us retrace our steps back through the door, into the garden, and up the staircase back into the current time and place. He took several minutes for us to reorient ourselves gently and to reflect on our experience. Then he asked those who were willing to share what they had experienced with the group. Several dramatic stories were told. I did not know what to make of it all.

I did not share my own experience. I was not sure how to evaluate it. Perhaps it was just the result of an overactive imagination. My rational, scientific background had me looking desperately for some explanation other than a past-life recall. I could explain the mountain setting by remembering scenes from a Himalayan trek. What seemed to be a Buddhist monastery might relate to pictures in books I had read about Buddhism. And the reference to Jon Kabat-Zinn could relate to my past contacts with him at UMass Medical School where we were both on the faculty. Still, it was all a bit unsettling. I had always felt a warmth and closeness to Jon that he seemed to reciprocate and that seemed to go beyond what one might reasonably expect from our limited contacts. And where did my interest in Buddhism come from?

The next day I signed up for a totally different experience: identifying animal tracks in the tropical forest around Maho Bay. After some preliminary instructions we were sent out in two-person teams to search for animal tracks. My partner for the exercise was a forty-ish Emergency Room nurse from a busy New York hospital. I recognized her as a fellow participant in Brian Weiss's session the previous day. It was a long afternoon, and we did not find many animal tracks. We had plenty of time to talk about other things, particularly her nursing career and my career in surgery. We developed a good rapport because of our joint medical background. The nurse was a down-to-earth, no-nonsense person. I thought that it would be interesting to inquire if she had experienced any hint of a past life in response to Brian Weiss's guided self-hypnotic suggestions the day before.

"Did you get any past-life images in yesterday's session with Brian Weiss?"

"Frankly, Brownie, I don't know. But I certainly had a weird and vivid dream that I would be glad to share, if you are interested."

"I certainly am. Please tell me."

"Well, do you remember when Dr. Weiss took us through a door and told us we were in a different time and place? At that moment I looked around. The land was flat and covered with snow and ice. Dr. Weiss said to look at our feet, and I did. I was wearing boots made out of animal skin with the fur inside. He said to look at our hands. The appearance of my hands shocked me. They were dark and coarse and callused. They were the hands of a workingman. Then suddenly my perspective shifted. I could see a man whom I recognized from his fur clothing as an Eskimo, and I knew that man was I. I was carrying a heavy club and was out hunting. Isn't that weird?

"From that point on, it was as though I was watching a dream unfold. I saw the Eskimo hunter walk over the bleak winter landscape, looking for prey. I wondered what prey could possibly be living in those barren fields of snow and ice. Suddenly, the man stopped, his eyes fixed on something in the distance. I followed his gaze and could see open water with a dark form stretched out on the shore. I knew instinctively that the dark form was a seal, but how in the world could the man hope to kill it? His only weapon was a club, and there was nothing to hide his approach from the animal. Surely when the seal saw the hunter getting close, it would plunge into the ocean and be safe.

"The Eskimo dropped to his knees. I could sense that he was speaking silently to the seal: Oh, Brother Seal, hear my plea! My children are hungry. They have no food. They are cold. They need new fur coats. Oh, Brother Seal, you could feed and clothe my children with your body. If you would only give us your body, we would always be grateful to you. Brother Seal, you could live forever in us. We would always honor you. Oh, Brother Seal, hear my plea!

"The seal did not move, but it seemed to me that the animal had heard the hunter's fervent plea. Ever so slowly, the hunter began to take small steps toward the seal. Finally, when he was only a few feet away, the Eskimo took a sudden leap and brought his club crashing down on the animal's head, killing it instantly. He stood there, breathing heavily for a moment, and then he hoisted the seal onto one shoulder and started for home.

"Isn't that the weirdest dream you ever heard?" she asked me.

"It's really weird, all right." I agreed. "Where in the world did it come from? I have read of some American Indians praying to animals they were hunting, calling them Brother Deer, for example. Have you ever read anything like that?"

"No, I don't know anything about Indians, much less Eskimos."

"It's a strange story. Why didn't you share it in the class when Dr. Weiss asked us to share our experiences?"

"I didn't know what to make of it, and I didn't want to make a fool out of myself in front of all those people."

I remembered that I did not feel like sharing my own experience, either.

So we left it at that. She wondered whether she could have relived a scene from a past life as an Eskimo hunter. Whether she could have been a man in that lifetime. If not, where did her remarkable "dream" come from?

I recalled a strange story I heard from a Mexican friend several years before. A brand-new hospital was being dedicated in Mexico City. The elaborate celebrations in honor of the occasion included a medical symposium with distinguished speakers. I was honored (and surprised) to be invited. On the program, I spoke

314

immediately after Dr. Michael DeBakey, a pioneer of cardiovascular surgery. I felt considerably upstaged, especially when the attractive wife of the President of Mexico, Madam Echeverria, came over to give Dr. DeBakey a big hug and kiss. I was in the seat next to the famous surgeon, and I didn't rate even a glance from the First Lady of Mexico.

I was the houseguest that week of Dr. Kuba Lichtinger, then-president of the Mexican chapter of the American College of Surgeons. Kuba and his wife were gracious and generous hosts, and I enjoyed getting to know their family. The youngest of their four sons was Victor, who lived with us the following summer. Victor's older brother, I believe his name was Peter, told me of a remarkable experience he had had recently.

Peter was driving through one of the oldest parts of Mexico City, where some houses dated back to the 16th century. The historic neighborhood felt strangely familiar to him. Suddenly, he saw a house that was more than familiar to him. With a jolt of recognition, he knew beyond any doubt that this house had once been his home. He could clearly picture the rooms inside, even though he had never seen this house or this neighborhood. The feeling of coming home was so powerful that he became consumed with the desire to look inside. He went to the front door and rang the bell.

After a few moments, a small peephole in the door opened, and a middle-aged woman scrutinized him carefully. "What do you want?" she said.

"I used to live here. And I would love to take a quick look around, if you would be kind enough to let me."

"This house has been in my family for many years. I do not believe you ever lived here."

People are cautious about letting a stranger in their home; Peter understood this. He thought quickly how he could convince the woman that he had once lived in her home. He began to describe the interior of the house to her, starting with the entry hall, proceeding to the drawing room, living room, dining room, and kitchen. He described the carved woodwork, the tile floors, and the beamed ceilings. Before he had finished, the door was silently opened, and the woman let him into the house. He had described its interior structure perfectly, except for the kitchen, which had been extensively renovated. The woman had no idea how the kitchen had looked before the renovations were carried out. She said that it was her understanding that the renovations had been completed over 150 years ago. She was amazed that Peter was able to describe the original kitchen. Peter was also amazed and puzzled. The Lichtingers were a secular Jewish family. They did not believe in an afterlife, much less reincarnation.

Kuba did not know how to explain his son's bizarre experience, but he was sure that his son would never make up such a strange tale. I did not know what to make of Peter's story, either. In 1972 I had never heard of past-lives recall; and I had heard very little about the deja-vu phenomenon or the possibility of reincarnation. I simply chalked up Peter's experience as one of life's infrequent and inexplicable happenings. Now, in the class on past-life therapy with Brian Weiss, I wondered if Peter had not experienced a flashback to an earlier lifetime in Old Mexico City. It was the only explanation I could think of.

The rest of the class was largely taken up with tales told under hypnosis by class volunteers. Brian Weiss selected the volunteers in part by asking them to roll their eyes up as far as they could. Some people could roll their eyes so far up that only the white sclera was visible. They were the best subjects. I could not roll my eyes up nearly that far, and Brian Weiss did not try to hypnotize me. I was just as glad not to be a subject. Under hypnosis, people told several interesting past-life stories, but I was not totally convinced of their validity. I wondered if they could simply be the result of a vivid imagination and perhaps a desire to please the group.

I was more convinced by Brian's recounting of his own experiences as a past-life therapist. He came across to me as honest and credible. A few of his patients had described past lives that could be verified objectively. Over the week, I had several brief personal conversations with Brian. Speaking to him one on one, I liked and trusted him.

The idea of reincarnation was relatively new and strange to me, but it is an old and familiar idea to much of humanity. It is a core belief of the Hindu and Buddhist religions. It was also a key belief of ancient Judaism and early Christianity. It is referred to in the Old Testament, the New Testament, the Hindu Bhagavad-Gita, the Buddhist Pali Canon, and many other sacred books.

Many psychoanalysts other than Brian Weiss have also encountered recall of past lives. The late Dr. Ian Stevenson, a professor of psychiatry at the University of Virginia, studied it extensively. His initial studies were carried out in children living in primitive societies, where they had no chance of programming through radio, TV, movies or other media and where the details in the presumed past life could be verified objectively. His first book, *20 Cases Suggestive of Reincarnation*, was rich in compelling case histories. He then went on to study past-life recall in many other places and eventually compiled thousands of cases. He was a respected academic, and his studies seemed well-designed. Like Brian Weiss, he was drawn into his first studies because of striking patient stories that he encountered in his clinical practice.

Another person whose work was credible to me was Dr. Helen Wambach, a psychologist at the Monmouth Medical Center in Long Branch, New Jersey, and a faculty member at the local community college. She was drawn into past-life studies by the personal experience of a vivid deja-vu phenomenon that strongly suggested a past-life recall. She then used hypnosis in large groups of people to facilitate their recall of past lives. Some of her subjects provided objective details that could be verified. Overall, Dr. Wambach compiled more than 1,000 cases of past-life recall. Her two books, *Recalling Past Lives* and *Life Before Life,* were published roughly 20 years before I met Brian Weiss. However, I had never heard of any such studies until meeting Brian Weiss in person. He piqued my curiosity about research in past-life recall. After reading his books, I went to the library and found that Ian Stevenson and Helen Wambach were only two of many psychologists who had written about patients with compelling past-life stories. I was quite surprised. Reincarnation seemed a remarkable concept to me, one with all sorts of implications for how we view our lives. Why isn't more scientific research being done in this field?

Why aren't more people curious about what Brian Weiss and his colleagues had to say? Why do we all quickly reject any unfamiliar idea that challenges our preconceptions? Meeting Brian Weiss was a wake-up call for me. It forced me to seriously consider the possibility of reincarnation. It is hard to take reincarnation seriously and not have it affect how you view death. And if we all have many lives, perhaps loss of the present one isn't as great a tragedy as we imagine.

THE LATE YEARS:
Making Peace With Mortality

CHAPTER 30

Seeking Comfort for the Spirit

—

One day I was making home visits with a hospice nurse, and we visited a 70-year-old woman dying of stomach cancer. Pale and emaciated, she was stretched out on a couch in the living room, propped up by pillows. Her husband was sitting on a straight-backed kitchen chair beside her. He was holding her hand.

She took one look at me and called out, "Why, Dr. Wheeler! What are you doing here?" She seemed surprised and delighted to see me, sick as she was. I wondered how she knew my name; but after a moment, I recognized her: She was Thelma L., a patient I had operated on ten years before to improve the circulation in her legs. She had done well after that surgery, and I had enjoyed seeing her on follow-up visits. Now she was dying of cancer, so emaciated she was hard to recognize as my former patient. I was glad that she seemed to regard my visit as a bright spot in her rapidly ebbing life.

"How are you today, Thelma?"

Her husband interrupted me, "Thelma is on her way to heaven, Doc!"

There was no regret in his remark. He was announcing a happy event. I was startled, since the remark seemed inappropriate to me.

"Soon she will be with the angels!" he added, just

in case I didn't get it the first time. "And one day, before long, I will meet her there." He was serious. They were devout Catholics and absolutely firm in their faith.

I tried to get on a more usual and comfortable topic for me. "Do you have any pain, Thelma?"

She replied, "The pain meds are a big help, but I still have a lot of pain when I eat." I thought to myself that the cancer probably involved her stomach and upper small bowel. It was easy to understand why eating would cause pain.

"If it hurts, then why do you eat? Are you hungry?"

"No, I have no appetite."

"Then why do you eat, if it causes you pain?"

She had no reply. She and her husband had just assumed that eating was good for her, even though they knew she was dying. She was relieved to know that she did not have to do anything that caused her pain, even eating or drinking.

The hospice nurse told me later that Thelma stopped eating after our visit. She did not drink much either. In about a week, she slipped into a coma and died peacefully. Her family was with her. They were glad that her suffering was over, and they were confident of a family reunion in heaven. Their faith was a great comfort to them.

Many patients find comfort in their religious beliefs. Others derive comfort from their own spiritual philosophy. There are many paths to peace with mortality. My own religious path started in a Methodist Sunday school in a small town in eastern Kentucky. It was a traditional Protestant church. The ultimate source of authority was the Bible. From time to time, the church sponsored revival meetings with visiting evangelists. They were passionate preachers who were absolutely sure of a Christian theology in which sin and Satan and hell played prominent roles. I hated those revival meetings! They made me feel guilty.

I was a childhood religious skeptic. My father told me once that when I was four years old, I asked him, "Where does God live?" Surprised, he thought for a moment and replied, "Everywhere!"

I pointed to a large rock lying nearby, and asked "Does God live in that rock?" He paused a moment and said, "Yes."

I replied, "I don't believe God lives in that rock."

My father let the matter drop. He was not about to debate abstruse theology with a four-year-old.

Despite my doubts, I revered the loving Jesus portrayed in that Methodist Sunday school: the Jesus who loved little children, who said to love our neighbors as ourselves, who even urged us to love our enemies. I was inspired by stories about the good Samaritan and the prodigal son. But as a teenager, Christian dogma repelled me. I could not believe that we all are born in original sin and that we are doomed to spend eternity in hell unless redeemed by faith in the resurrection of Christ. What about children in far-off lands who had never heard of Jesus? What sort of Father God would inflict pain on those innocent children? And the miracles described in the New Testament were hard for me to believe. The fundamental beliefs of Protestant Christianity just didn't make sense to me. So I gradually broke away from Christianity, while still inspired by the teachings of Jesus.

For many years organized religion played a minor

role in my life. That began to change when Betty and I got married and had children. We felt that our children should at least know the history of the Judeo-Christian tradition on which our Western civilization is largely based. We also felt they should be made aware of all the major religions of the world. We joined a Unitarian church. There was no dogma, and we were free to believe whatever our conscience dictated. Our children could attend a liberal and ecumenical Sunday school.

We explored other faiths. I was particularly drawn to Buddhism. I liked the Buddha's denial that he had any unique personal divinity. I also liked his encouragement to explore whatever seems true to you and not trust blindly in his teachings. I liked his emphasis on meditation and living in the moment. I liked his emphasis on kindness and compassion. I liked his belief that there is no sin, just ignorance and "unskillful behavior," which leads to bad karma rather than the punishments of hell.

Betty and I attended Buddhist sittings, and we went to a weeklong retreat with Thich Nhat Hahn. We also went to several symposia where the Dalai Lama was the keynote speaker. At a conference we attended at Massachusetts Institute of Technology, His Holiness said that Buddhism is not a dogmatic religion but a science of the mind, open to change if new scientific findings compel it to do so. At Brandeis University, he said that his true religion was kindness. At the Daughters of the American Revolution Constitution Hall in Washington, DC, he stressed the importance of science and Buddhism working together to understand consciousness. Betty and I liked the concept of a religion based on kindness and open to scientific study.

We also found much wisdom in the Hindu religion, and we went on a weeklong retreat with Ram Das. We learned a bit about Sufism on a retreat with Pir Vilayet Inayat Khan. The more that we found out about the world's major religions, the more we learned they all had much to offer.

I am reminded of an experience from our Himalayan trek in 1985. It happened at the end of our 17-day hike, after we had returned to a hotel in Katmandu. The last night we had a farewell dinner with our fellow trekkers, shared a few hugs, and said our goodbyes. The next morning we packed our bags, which didn't take long since we had not been allowed to bring much on the trek. Betty was done with her packing not long after breakfast. We didn't have to leave for the airport until late afternoon, so she decided that she would wander around the street markets and look for some last-minute presents for friends and family. As usual, I was a bit slower than she was, but I finished my packing with a few hours to spare. I decided to take a walk through the shop district.

Not far from the hotel was an art gallery with a front window display of some dramatic oil paintings of the Himalayas. I went in to look at the art. The gallery was small, about 20 feet square, and its walls were covered with beautiful oil and watercolor paintings of the highest mountains in the world. I thought that I would enjoy seeing one of those mountain scenes on my office wall and remembering the trek.

No one was in the gallery when I entered, but soon a dark-haired, dark-skinned man came out of a back room. He introduced himself as the gallery owner and the artist of many of the paintings. In the course of conversation, he mentioned his spiritual master, a famous Hindu holy man. I was curious to learn more, and I asked many questions. The gallery owner seemed delighted to have a Western physician so interested in knowing about his religion and his spiritual master. He offered to close his gallery for the day and take me to visit the jungle retreat where his master had spent the last years of his life—a life that ended in 1963 at the truly remarkable age of 137.

Unfortunately, I could not go to the forest retreat, because I had to leave shortly to catch a plane home. The gallery owner was disappointed but talked to me at length about his guru, known as the Shivapuri Baba. He gave me a biography written by an Englishman who was a student of world religions and whose spiritual search finally led him to Nepal and the Shivapuri Baba. The biography had a striking head-and-shoulders photograph of the holy man on its cover. His piercing dark eyes riveted my attention. His gaze was slightly upward, as though he was seeing some deeply satisfying vision. His faint smile seemed to radiate inner peace. His dark skin showed few wrinkles, and his jet-black hair and beard had only the lightest sprinkling of gray. This seemed quite remarkable because the caption said that the picture was taken when the Shivapuri Baba was 112 years old.

The gallery owner also gave me about 40 pages he had typed of his master's teachings. He firmly refused to accept any payment for these gifts. He also presented me with a beautiful watercolor he had painted of Makalu, the fifth highest mountain in the world and one of the most beautiful. I was greatly touched by his generosity, and I remember vividly the story he told of his master's life.

The Shivapuri Baba felt that following a specific

religion was not essential for a person's spiritual growth, although it was helpful for most people. The gallery owner tried to explain the role of world religions to me as the Shivapuri Baba had explained it to him. To the best of my recollection, this is what he said:

All rivers flow to the sea. Some flow in a straighter path than others, but all eventually reach the sea. In the same way, all religions lead at last to God. Some take a more direct path than others, but all reach God in the end. What matters is not the path taken, but the earnestness of the seeker.

The Baba's words, as relayed through his artist devotee, rang true to me. I had always felt that there was some truth in all religions. I had also felt that no one religion had the whole truth. The Shivapuri Baba, an enlightened Hindu saint, reached the same conclusion but with infinitely more spiritual experience and insight to justify his views. It was reassuring.

I have learned to respect all religions, including the Christianity that I once rejected. I take comfort in the fact that similar religious beliefs have risen in widely separated places at widely different times throughout human history. All religions honor the Golden Rule in one way or another. They believe in a Supreme Power and an afterlife. Buddhism and Hinduism believe in reincarnation, as did early Christians and Jews. The widespread nature of all these beliefs seems to indicate some credibility or at least a common need to which they are responding.

I now regard Jesus as a great wisdom teacher— perhaps the greatest of all — in the company of the Buddha, Moses, Confucius, Lao-tse, Muhammad, and the Vedic masters of ancient India. Much historical and scholarly research about early Christianity has occurred during my lifetime. It was greatly stimulated by the chance discovery of long-hidden ancient manuscripts: the Gnostic Gospels, buried in Egypt and found by peasant farmers in 1945; the pre-Christian scrolls of the Essenes, found in 1946 by a shepherd boy in caves overlooking the Dead Sea; the lost Gospel Q, which biblical scholars deduced by analyzing the language and structure of the New Testament gospels Matthew, Mark, Luke, and John. It has been fascinating for me to read why some ancient gospels were accepted for inclusion in the New Testament, whereas others were rejected. The early church fathers selected gospels that supported their own beliefs, and they branded as heresy those that did not. Believing in the truth of a book that the Roman Catholic Church had decreed heretical, heretical might have caused an unlucky believer to be burned at the stake.

I have read much about how early Christianity developed. The earliest manuscripts (the Gnostic Book of Thomas and the lost Gospel Q, both written circa 50 AD) consist solely of the *teachings* of Jesus. There is no mention of his life story—or any of the religious dogma that troubled me as a child. The earliest followers of Jesus valued his teachings; they were much less interested in his personal history. They referred to their religion as "The Way" not as the "Christian" church.

The gospels selected for the New Testament were written later than the Gospel Q or the Book of Thomas. As they became further removed in time from the life of Jesus, the stories they told of his life and death become more and more colorful. In the Book of John, the last New Testament gospel written, Jesus is actually portrayed as God incarnate, a status that Jesus never claimed for himself in the earliest gospels. That claim of divinity must have been difficult for some of the earliest followers of Jesus to accept. It wasn't until the fourth century that the Book of John finally was added to the list of "approved" books in the New Testament, due to the aggressive sponsorship of the fiery and powerful Bishop Athanasius of Alexandria. (Much of this information comes from the books of religious historians, especially Elaine Pagels, a professor of religion at Princeton, and Karen Armstrong, a British religious historian.)

I expect some beliefs will comfort me when death is approaching. For years, I would not have thought to include religious beliefs. Yet I have always been intrigued by spirituality, including not only religion but also so-called paranormal phenomena: near-death experiences, communication with the dead by mediums, past-life memories under hypnotic regression, precognitive dreams, and other psychic experiences that are hard to explain.

I have come to realize that there is no clear separation between religion and spirituality. Religion can provide spiritual comfort. The teachings of Jesus—as well as those of Buddha, Lao-tse, Muhammad, ancient Hindu masters, and other religious leaders—can bring peace and guidance, both for living and for dying.

I have memorized favorite passages from religious literature to use as mantras for meditation. I began doing this when I was on long airplane trips to medical meetings, and I wanted to pass the time in a constructive way. When I had finished any paper work that I had to do, I usually read books. One of my favorite books to read at such times was written by an Indian professor named Eknath Easwaran. He advocated memorizing favorite passages from the world's great religious literature and repeating them as a meditative practice. I decided to try it. From the Judeo-Christian tradition, I memorized the Sermon on the Mount, the prayer of St. Francis, the 23rd Psalm, and the Lord's Prayer. From the Buddhist tradition, I memorized the Twin Verses from the Dhammapada. From the Hindu Vedas, I memorized the Rig Veda and the Katha Upanishad. Simply repeating the words of the world's greatest religious teachings calms and comforts me. I believe this will also be true as I approach death.

For most of my life, I have not followed a traditional religious path. Neither have I worried about the literal truth of any one religion. They all seemed partly true to me, but none seemed wholly true. The common beliefs of various religions seemed more important than their differences. I felt that we should each choose our own religious path, whichever seems right to us. My personal beliefs are an amalgam of liberal Christianity, leavened by the teachings of several other faith traditions. I am comfortable with that mix, and I expect to be comfortable with it when I die.

This chapter is a purely personal statement. It may not resonate comfortably with readers who have different religious beliefs, but I respect all spiritual paths. I do not claim any special insights or credentials beyond what is in this book. I am not a philosopher or a psychologist or a theologian or even a well-informed scientist. I do not consider myself an expert on death and dying, and my spiritual beliefs have changed profoundly during my lifetime. I have worked out a set of beliefs that seems right to me, at least for now. Prominent among them is the belief that there are some things we will never know. As the channel medium said, "You are not here to explain life, but to experience it."

CHAPTER 31

Myth, Insight and Religion

—

I have known all I really need to know for a long time. All living things mature, reproduce themselves, deteriorate with time, cease to function, and die. Their places are taken by their offspring, who follow the same life course. This pattern is built into the laws of nature. Life is inevitably followed by death. Perhaps I should say that death of the body is inevitable. But what about the spirit? What about our individual consciousness, or whatever it is that gives each of us our unique identity? For many ages, all over the world, religions and philosophers have drawn a distinction between body and spirit. The question then arises: If the body dies, does the spirit die too?

I believe that the spirit does not die. My belief is based in large part on the experiences recounted in this book, rather than religious dogma or scientific conclusions. Still, I am reassured that belief in survival of the spirit is at the heart of the world's major religions. It is also expressed in myths and folklore, even in ancient archeology sites. At many different times in human history, in widely separated places, people have believed in survival of the spirit. That belief has been supported by abundant soft evidence: ghost stories, medium communications, past-life recall, near-death experiences, and other psychic insights consistent with survival of the spirit in some form. Such evidence is circumstantial in nature. It is not hard science. Still, it is impressive in its breadth and depth and in the commonality of such beliefs throughout human history.

I will never know all the answers to life's big questions. Nor will anyone else. The questions are too big, and our minds are too small. My mind cannot contain any concept of God. Similarly, my mind cannot comprehend the vast size and complexity of God's Creation. I have read that the cosmos contains an almost infinite number of galaxies and that each galaxy contains an almost infinite number of stars. Most stars are separated from us by distances so incredibly vast that they must be defined by the distance light can travel in a year. As I write this chapter, astronomers have just reported the discovery of a new exploding star, a so-called super nova, 140 million light years away. The speed of light is 186,000 miles a second. Can you imagine how impossibly far away that cosmic explosion must have been? Or how incredibly long ago it took place?

I cannot conceive that the universe goes on forever. Neither can I conceive that it stops somewhere. What would lie beyond? To complicate matters, scientists now tell us that time and space are only illusions. New perceptions of reality have been introduced by modern physics: quantum theory, relativity, string theory, parallel universes, and dark matter. A relatively recent discovery, dark matter is said to comprise most of the physical matter in the cosmos. But if dark matter is most of the substance of the universe, why did scientists overlook it for so long? And who knows what other startling scientific insights into the nature of reality will be discovered in the years ahead? I never expect to understand it all, but I do not worry about my lack of understanding anymore.

A few centuries ago, the sun and stars were thought to revolve around the Earth. It was a common-sense belief, one that you could confirm with your own eyes. During the day, you could see the sun rotate across the sky. And at night, the stars also rotated around the dark sky. What could be a more obvious truth? But now we know better. Similarly, a few centuries hence, I have no doubt that some of our own self-evident truths will seem just as mistaken as the ancient view of the sun's rotation around the Earth.

As a surgeon, I find the human body just as amazing as the cosmos. How can a single fertilized cell develop into the infinitely complex human body? Where does consciousness come from? How does the body know how to heal a unique and complex injury? Or fight off a life-threatening infection? We have learned an incredible amount about how the body works, and we will doubtless learn much more through science. I am a firm believer in the scientific method and its ability to unravel secrets that seem inexplicable today. And I believe in evolution. How-ever, no matter how much we learn, there will always be a limit to our scientific knowledge. Beyond that limit there are mysteries that fill me with awe and reverence, a feel-ing that brings me to wonder about the existence of God.

Do I believe in God? To answer that question in a meaningful way, I would have to define just what is meant by the word God. And there the question breaks down for me. I cannot begin to define God. Any deity or primal force capable of creating the universe and the human body and all the laws that govern this infinitely complex creation is much too big for my small mind to grasp. I cannot believe that the star-filled skies and the wonders of the natural world are due to chance. Neither can I conceive of a Creator who made it all.

I am reminded of a story from the Bhagavad-Gita, a sacred text of the Hindu religion. The story is about Arjuna, a warrior prince in an ancient Indian kingdom. Arjuna is the leader of an army preparing for battle against an invading force commanded by his own relatives. He has no heart for the battle. He does not want to kill his uncles and cousins. Discouraged, he surveys the site for the coming battle from his war chariot. He shares his tormented feelings with his wise chariot driver, who is in reality the Hindu god Krishna, disguised in a human form.

Krishna urges Arjuna to fight. He says that death is only an illusion: The spirit is immortal, even if the body perishes. The spirit will be reborn in a new body. He describes the goals of life on Earth and the need to fight for a worthy cause. Arjuna quickly realizes that his chariot driver is no ordinary mortal, but the god Krishna in disguise. He begs Krishna to reveal himself in all the glory of his divine form. Krishna says that the unshielded sight of God would be too much for him to bear, but Arjuna pleads further. Finally, Krishna shows himself to Arjuna in all the blinding splendor of his divine form, which contains everything, everywhere: beautiful and ugly, alive and dead, kind and cruel, all things that are, ever were, or ever will be. The sight is dazzling beyond comprehension. Awestruck and terrified, Arjuna begs Krishna to return to his human form.

Like Arjuna, I would like to have a glimpse of God, whatever God may be. But also like Arjuna, I doubt that I could bear the sight. An omnipotent, omniscient, omnipresent God is totally beyond my comprehension. Indefinable. Unknowable. Still, the fingerprints of God are everywhere. I have seen them in unexpected places. Let me give you an example. In late November and early December of 1985, Betty and I went on a 17-day trek in the Himalaya Mountains of Nepal. My good friend Jim Foster, an avid mountain climber, organized the trek. Jim was chief of surgery at Hartford Hospital, and he and I had many professional contacts over the years. He had climbed mountains all over the world, including the Himalayas. Once, between working sessions at a meeting of the directors of the American Board of Surgery, Jim and I talked about our mutual love of mountain hiking. He offered to organize a private family trek in Nepal. It would include my wife, Betty; Jim's wife, Sally; our friend and fellow board member Alex Walt; and any of our children or close friends who were free to join us. I was extremely enthusiastic. I was 56 years old and felt that it was probably my last chance to trek in the Himalayas. Betty had some reservations about the physical challeng-es, but she finally agreed to come, as did our son Stephen. By the time we left Kathmandu in a dilapidated bus, our trekking group had swelled to 16 family members and friends.

We started the trek in Pokara, the last town that could be reached by road. Eight Sherpa guides and 45 porters joined us there: a real expedition. Our goal, many miles away, was a glacial cirque known as the Annapurna Sanctuary. A high mountain valley ringed by 11 mountains over 20,000 feet high, the sanctuary is the base camp for climbing the south face of Annapurna, an imposing mass of near-vertical rock and one of the world's ten highest mountains.

Betty and me on our 1985 trek to Annapurna (seen in background: 26,645 feet high)

Several days into the trek, we arrived at Poon Hill. Though only 11,000 feet high, its crest provides a spectacular vantage point from which to see some of the highest mountains. We pitched our faded red-brown pup tents at about 10,000 feet. A few miles to the east, Poon Hill faced the rocky mass of south Annapurna, nearly 25,000 feet high. Behind it loomed the three peaks of the main massif with Annapurna 1 topping out at 26,545 feet. A few miles to the west, across the Khali Gandaki Gorge—the deepest gorge on the planet—was the equally massive form of Dhauligiri, the world's sixth highest mountain at 26,643 feet. Many other mountains around the perimeter, though not quite so high and not so famous, were also beautiful and awesome. Our trekking party spent an entire afternoon atop Poon Hill, taking pictures and feeling fortunate to see this glorious panorama on a sparkling clear December day.

That night I had trouble sleeping, as I struggled to keep warm in the bitter cold. Fully clothed and zipped inside two mummy sleeping bags, I felt as though I was in a straightjacket. Lying awake, about three a.m., I realized that if I started climbing then I could be on the top of Poon Hill before the sun came up. Seeing sunrise over the Himalayas should be quite spectacular, I thought, and should provide some remarkable photo opportunities. The thought of going up the mountain trail alone in the dark was intimidating, as was the bitter cold, but the prospect seemed worth the risk. So I wiggled out of the warm mummy bags and started up the trail.

I warmed up as I climbed, and I reached the top just as the sky was starting to lighten. I was completely alone, the solitary witness to the awesome spectacle of great mountains waking up to a new day. I set up my camera on a tripod and waited. The sky above the mountains slowly brightened. After a few minutes, a pale shaft of sunlight pierced the sky on the north side of Annapurna and quickly grew brighter. A similar streak of light appeared on the South side. I took some pictures as the outline of the peak became rimmed with light.

Before long, a brilliant sliver of sun appeared on the side of Annapurna. Behind me, the crest of Dhauligiri was already radiant in bright sunlight, dramatically highlighted above the dark mass of that huge mountain, still mainly in the shade. It was a magical scene. I stood and watched the awe-inspiring panorama: the brilliant red-orange sunrise, the pale blue sky with its sun-splashed clouds, and the great mountains at daybreak, partly in early morning sunlight and partly in lingering darkness of the departing night.

The sun rose rapidly. It was, all too soon, time to go back to camp. Reluctantly, I started down the trail. Before long, I saw eight small tents far below me on the mountainside. Faded and rusty in color, those pup tents were quite cramped for two people, only about three feet high in front and even lower in back.

No one was up. I was still alone with the Himalayas at daybreak. I hated to break the spell, so I sat down on a rock to watch the remaining sunrise. A short distance below me was a tiny, one-person tent, pitched well away from the main camp, where Ang Nema, our head Sherpa, slept. A soft, barely audible chant was coming from the tent. Ang Nema, a devout Buddhist, was saying his morning prayers. It seemed to me like a fitting way to welcome the new day.

I sat there in solitude on the mountainside, listening to the soft chanting, deeply moved by the splendor of that sunrise over the Himalayas. My mind was totally absorbed by the scene. I had no conscious thoughts, no theological insights, no celestial visions, but it was a profound spiritual experience. I did not wonder about the existence of a God who had created those magnificent mountains. It would have seemed a silly question. God was all around me.

I have had similar feelings at other times when I have sensed an awesome, but unseen presence behind the beauty of the natural world. For example, once I took a canoe out for a night paddle on Sebago Lake in Maine. It was a beautiful summer night. There were no lights from cottages or stores. That part of the lake was protected from development, since it was the watershed for drinking water for the city of Portland. The lake was dark and deserted. There was no moon, and the stars were unusually bright and close. The lake was completely still. No boats. No wind. No waves. It was totally peaceful.

I paddled out into the lake for a few minutes, but I had no desire to paddle any farther. The night was meant for silence and stillness and solitude. I stretched out in the bottom of the canoe and looked up at the bright stars in the night sky. After a while, I felt as though I were dissolving into the scene. The stars seemed to sink down and cover me. Or did my spirit expand up into the stars? I seemed to be a part of everything, and everything seemed to be a part of me. I felt in touch with a vast, incomprehensible presence, a presence that I might as well call God.

Another time, Betty and I were hiking through a redwood forest in a northern California state park. It was early morning and the sun had not yet burned off the fog. Giant ferns were still wet with dew. The massive trunks of ancient redwood trees disappeared into the fog a hundred feet or so up. It was a scene that could have been unchanged for a thousand years or a million years. I would not have been surprised to see a dinosaur stick its head out from behind one of the giant redwoods. Once again, I felt the presence of God all around me.

I have had similar feelings in many scenes of great natural beauty. When scuba diving, I have been filled with awe while watching schools of brightly colored fish swim lazily around a coral reef. I have also felt something transcendent under less dramatic circumstances: when struck by the extravagant beauty of a freshly opened white peony or the rich red petals of a rose … or the striking geometric designs and beautiful colors on a butterfly's wing …

or the simple grace of a seagull soaring effortlessly in a strong sea wind. Why is the world of nature so beautiful? Surely God must be playing!

I have also experienced a sense of something sacred, something awesome in inspired human creations. I have felt it while sitting in the stillness of Chartres Cathedral, watching the rays of the late afternoon sun stream through its stained glass windows, igniting the luminous blue colors for which it is famous. I have felt uplifted by great music or art: listening to the Mozart's Requiem or looking at Michelangelo's Pieta in St. Peter's Basilica.

And I have sensed a profound spiritual presence in the hospital delivery room at the moment of birth, of the first breath, when a new life is just beginning. Or when I was standing by a patient's bedside at the moment of death, of the last breath, when a life has drawn to its close. I have sometimes sensed that same presence in other people and even in myself when meditating. Thomas Merton, a Trappist monk and a well-known writer, once wrote that he never felt so close to God as when he was deeply absorbed in meditating on his own breath, as Buddhists do.

I believe something sacred exists in each one of us. This is a lesson I was taught by Nepalese peasants whom we passed on mountain trails when we were trekking in the Himalayas. Part of the trek was on the main trail used for commerce between Tibet and Nepal. From time to time, we encountered a train of burros loaded with yak wool. The peasants were traveling from high mountain pastures to the town of Pokara to barter their wool for salt, spices, and other basic supplies. If we were on a steep mountainside, we had to hug the inside face of the cliff so that the heavily loaded burros did not force us over the outside face—and a fall to the rocks far below. The encounters were scary at times.

The yak herders who controlled the burros seemed to come from a different world. I doubt if their home-made clothing had changed for centuries. Their faces and hands were baked brown by the sun, wrinkled and leathery. More often than not, they were missing some front teeth and those that remained were heavily stained. I could not imagine what their lives must be like, and doubtless they could not imagine mine either. Still, we were all human beings, our circumstances changed only by the chance of where we were born.

As they approached us on the path, the yak herders would put their hands together in prayer position, bow their heads slightly in our direction, smile gently, and softly say, "Namaste." It was a warm and friendly greeting. After experiencing this a few times, I began to send their message back, including that strange greeting, namaste. After a while, I became curious as to the meaning of namaste. I asked Ang Nema what the greeting meant. After thinking a moment and choosing his words care-fully, he said, namaste means "the light within me honors the light within you." How beautiful, I thought, and what a lot of meaning in only three syllables!

I thought of the Quakers who believe that a spark of the divine glows in each of us. Or the Buddhists who believe that we all have Buddha nature hidden in our hearts. Or the Hindus who believe that we all contain the "atman," our individual part of the universal "Atman" (expressed in English as the individual "self," part of the universal "Self.") I find it comforting to think that we all have a spark of the divine within us. I like thinking that the weather-beaten Nepalese yak herders we passed on a Himalayan path believe that they each contain a light of the divine within them. And that they share that light with me and everyone else, that we all have the same sacred spark, that despite our many differences, there is a common divinity in us all. I enjoyed returning their greeting, putting my hands together in prayer position, bowing to them, and saying, "Namaste," while thinking to myself, "The light within me honors the light within you."

Behind this world we see, I have felt the presence of something much bigger than we are, something others might call God. Something I cannot explain, but that I have experienced. That presence does not feel cold and withdrawn to me. It feels warm, benign, conscious, and comforting. Even loving. I can't tell you where these feelings come from. I won't try to justify them. But they feel right to me. I cannot believe that the world exists by chance. I believe that behind it all is something incomprehensible, a creative presence that can be sensed at moments of peak insight. I have sensed it in nature, in art, and in other people. I no longer find it necessary to believe or disbelieve in any specific concept of God or an afterlife. Whatever is true is true. Whatever will be, will be: regardless of what I wish or what I believe. It does not matter what I think.

It seems clear that life in the physical body becomes increasingly undesirable as the body and mind deteriorate and lose their ability to function. Death can be not only inevitable, but also welcome. At worst, death can still provide relief from suffering, "a sleep from which the sleeper does not wake," as Socrates said. At best, death is the doorway to a happy afterlife: the heaven of Christians, the paradise of Muslims, the nirvana of Buddhists, the happy hunting grounds of Native Americans, or some other unimaginable continuation of consciousness in another realm.

In matters that science cannot prove or disprove in the laboratory, such as the existence of God or an afterlife, what can we believe on faith, based largely on circumstantial evidence: near-death experiences, ghost stories, medium communications, hallucinogenic drugs, past-life recall under hypnosis, and so on? I used to be quite skeptical of faith, particularly in matters of religious dogma. I relied instead on science to verify my beliefs. But the methods of science and its most sacrosanct tenets change with time too. A century ago, the nature of reality was firmly based on the Newtonian theory of a clockwork universe. That worldview gave way to Einstein's theory of relativity and Max Planck's quantum mechanics. Who knows what lies beyond quantum theory? And who is to say that there may not be some ways other than the scientific laboratory to understand the nature of reality? Intuition, gut feelings, psychic perceptions, and even mystical insights may have some validity, although I realize the need to maintain a healthy skepticism and to avoid becoming gullible or superstitious.

Somewhat to my surprise and relief, my life experiences have left me with a faith that brings me comfort. I believe that the universe did not come about by chance. Neither did human life. Behind our life on Earth, I believe there is a purpose, hazy though it may be. I believe that our spirit survives the death of our body—

and that the spirit lives on in a different realm. Perhaps the spirit even returns to Earth in a new body. I believe that behind all that we see is a vast creative intelligence that we can sense at peak moments. And I believe that it is benign and loving in nature, despite the suffering we see in the world around us.

I no longer worry about finding convincing answers to Life's Big Questions. Many people have tried and failed to find those answers. Others have adopted answers that are definitive, but differ sharply from each other. Obviously, answers that conflict with each other cannot all be true. I am content with stopping to search for Ultimate Truths that are too big for me to grasp. If that attitude seems to be a copout, so be it. And if a reader continues to press for my core beliefs, I would simply say that we are all sparks of the divine, and that our spirits are eternal, though housed in bodies that are transient. I believe that the eternal spirit lives on after death of the transient body. It may live on in a different form or in a very different realm, or it may return to Earth in a new body. I see little point in speculating about matters we cannot fully comprehend. Finally, I believe that life on Earth is good, that it has a purpose and that in the end all will be well.

Whatever we believe, we should all be grateful for the gift of life on this Earth. What a blessing! We should be grateful for the beauty of the natural world. I am grateful for the chance to love others and to be loved by them. I am grateful for the chance to help others. For many reasons, I believe that life on Earth is a great gift. But I also believe that behind the world we see is an unseen world, a world that we cannot perceive directly, but that is real nevertheless. At peak moments, I can sense its presence, even though it remains hidden from my eyes.

Different paths lead to peace in the face of death. My own path is composed mainly of insights that have taken shape from the experiences described in this book. They have provided comfort to me, and I hope they will also bring comfort to my readers. I have learned that we don't need to have all the answers to life's big questions in order to be comfortable with death. We are not here to explain life, but to experience it. There is a reassuring order that governs the universe. Death is part of that order. It is an inescapable part of life. It is natural. It is necessary. I have come to believe that for most of us, death is a blessing.

CHAPTER 32

My Own Death

—

In June of 2006, I was diagnosed with Parkinson's disease, a progressive disorder that damages the nervous system. It can be treated but not cured. It can end in severe disability, dementia, and death, unless some unrelated disease or injury takes the person's life first. The time course is variable and sometimes many years long. This chapter is my story to date, and my best guess about the future.

—

The first warning sign was my handwriting. It became cramped and progressively smaller. The script was shaky and hard to read. It looked like the writing of a feeble old man. But I didn't feel like a feeble old man! What was happening? Writing legibly—once so easy— required a conscious effort. I had to concentrate hard on what I was writing if I wanted it to be legible and a reasonable size. Even my signature, so often repeated and once so routine, now required an effort to look normal. I sometimes had to sign diplomas or certificates that would later hang proudly on some young doctor's office wall. I was anxious for my signature to look normal. Sometimes I would practice signing my name several times before signing the actual document.

I also began to notice trouble with other fine

motor skills: Typing errors at the computer keyboard became more common. Tying my shoelaces required more time and thought. Doing up the buttons on my shirts took more time as well. It was frustrating! Everything that I did to get dressed in the morning seemed to take more time and effort than it once had. For no apparent reason, I was slowing down in my daily activities. I also noticed a slight cough at meals. Observing that cough closely, I realized that my swallowing motions were sometimes not well coordinated. They allowed a few drops of liquid to spill into my windpipe.

What bothered me most was that my speech became softer and sometimes slurred. Not infrequently, someone I was talking to would ask me to repeat what I had just said. It sounded almost like I had had too much to drink. It was embarrassing! Something was clearly wrong, but I was not at all sure what it was. I made an appointment to see Dr. Peter Gordon, my primary care physician. After hearing my story and doing a physical examination, Peter was also uncertain about the exact cause, but he thought that something must be wrong with my nervous system. He suggested a consultation with Dr. K, a respected neurologist. It took a few weeks to get an appointment.

Finally, the day arrived when I met the consultant. Dr. K was about 50 years old. His short, dark hair was sprinkled with gray. His overall appearance was neat and professional but without any medical props or pretense. He was in his own office environment, he was comfortable there, and he was firmly in control. His job was to identify the cause of my symptoms and not necessarily to hold my hand in the process. On first meeting, Dr. K was reassuring in his professional manner but not especially warm or empathetic. I felt a bit like a butterfly displayed on a pin, being observed closely and classified precisely by a butterfly expert.

He took a brief medical history and then performed a more detailed neurological examination: strength, balance, reflexes, eye movements, and so on. He seemed particularly interested in my difficulty in doing rapid alternating movements with my right hand: touching my thumb to my index finger as rapidly as I could, releasing and then repeating again and again, as fast as I could. Or slapping my right thigh first with the palm and then the back of my right hand, back and forth, back and forth, faster and faster. He timed how many repetitions I could do in 15 seconds. I was surprised at how slow I was. I felt as though I were flunking his test. Dr. K settled back in his chair and looked at me in silence for a minute. It made me uncomfortable. Finally, he said, "What are you most afraid of?"

I was surprised and stunned. Where did that question come from? Did I look afraid? What was he about to tell me? Without any conscious thought, I responded immediately, "Parkinson's disease." I wondered where that quick response came from. At some deep level, I must have been afraid that I might follow the tragic course of good friends who were then suffering severe disability, and even dementia, due to Parkinson's. Or perhaps I was thinking of other surgeon colleagues who had died of Parkinson's.

Dr. K responded immediately, without a hint of emotion, "That's right! That's what you have."

Bang! Right between the eyes! No gentle tiptoeing around the facts. No gradual easing into revealing a much-dreaded diagnosis. No attempt to soften the blow. My face must have reflected my dismay. Dr. K obviously noticed my reaction and tried to reassure me somewhat. He said that I had a slowly progressive form of the disease. He went on, "You will probably live with Parkinson's for the next 15 years and die from something entirely unrelated. There is no cure, but the progress can be slowed and the symptoms can be helped by medication."

I felt a bit better, but not much. At least Dr. K had said that the time course was long.

For the previous couple of years, every two or three weeks, I had visited Clem Hiebert, a longtime victim of Parkinson's disease and a good friend. I had known Clem since we were both students at Harvard Medical School. It had been painful for me to watch the inexorable progression of Clem's disease. Sitting in Dr. K's office that day, I was determined that Clem's fate would not be my fate too.

Clem Hiebert, as second-year Harvard Medical School student
Credit: Aesculapiad (Harvard Medical School Yearbook 1949)

Dr. K prescribed medication: Sinemet, a small, yellow tablet before each meal. I asked if he had any objection to adding alternative medicine treatments. He said that he had no objections, but there was no scientific evidence that they were of any benefit. I resolved to do anything and everything that had been claimed to help Parkinson's patients, regardless of whether the claims were supported by rigorous scientific studies or not. I knew how hard it was to get funding to study such treatment properly. I was willing to try whatever regimen claimed to be of benefit, even without hard proof, provided there were no serious side effects—and not too much expense.

Later, on the Internet, I found many diverse treatments that claimed to slow the progression of Parkinson's disease: a diet high in fresh fruits and vegetables, exercise, meditation, yoga, acupuncture, massage, Reiki treatments, and nutritional supplements. I decided to incorporate as many as practical into my treatment plan. And I have! Betty and I start each day with yoga, exercise and meditation. I work out with a personal trainer once a week and play tennis two or three times each week. We also walk from one to three miles on a beach near our home two or three times a week.

I have tried to exercise my mind, as well as my body. I have dabbled in Sudoku, Scrabble, crossword puzzles, and other mind games. Mostly, however, I have relied on writing this book as a creative mind game.

Each day, Betty and I eat several servings of fresh fruit and vegetables. We eat a moderate amount of seafood and only rarely do we eat red meat. We also supplement our diet with a broad-based program of multivitamins and minerals. Betty gives me a Reiki treatment about once a week, and I have an acupuncture appointment every three or four weeks. I was skeptical of the acupuncture at first, but I decided to keep an open mind. I definitely feel better after an acupuncture treatment, no matter what the explanation.

It has now been over eight years since Dr. K first broke the bad news. I saw him every six months. The visits became more relaxed. There were more smiles. I am grateful to him for identifying what was wrong with me. Some of my symptoms are a bit worse, but many are unchanged. I now have an occasional tremor of my right hand that has been present the last couple of years. When walking, I have a tendency to scuff my right heel and limp slightly, unless I take care to pick up my right foot. I am slower in many activities than before, but overall I feel quite lucky.

I still play a reasonable game of tennis, but only doubles because of two knee replacements. I am still recovering from the second knee procedure, but my tennis strokes are returning well, and I am looking forward to walking on a nearby beach with my wife.

My memory remains sharp, remarkably so, people say. I have not noticed any deterioration in my ability to write this book, whether relying on the sharpness of my memory, the creative writing, or the manual computer skills required. From my perspective, I see no need to increase my medication, although I recently went to another neurologist who recommended increasing the dosage. (Dr. K had moved out of the state.) All in all, I feel most fortunate!

Still, I want to do all I can to avoid Clem's fate.

Clem was one of the best surgeons I ever knew, but the disease gradually robbed him of his muscle coordination and his mental acuity. It was painful to observe.

I first got to know Clem Hiebert when I was a second-year medical student, living on the fourth floor of Vanderbilt Hall, the dormitory for Harvard medical students. Clem's room was next to mine, so I saw him a lot, even though Clem was one year ahead of me. Tall, lean, and bursting with energy, he attracted attention in any group. He had sandy hair and a high forehead, almost as though his brain was oversized and required extra space. From my perspective, Clem was a quintessential Big Man on Campus, a student leader who was involved with all the significant student organizations and activities.

After graduating from medical school in 1951, he trained in surgery at Massachusetts General Hospital. One year behind Clem, I trained in surgery at the Peter Bent Brigham Hospital, another Harvard teaching hospital; and we kept in touch from time to time. We had more of a chance to get together in England in 1956–1957, when Clem had a surgical fellowship in Cambridge and I was doing a similar fellowship in London. We were both married by then, and the Hieberts had an infant son.

As our surgical careers progressed, Clem and I were active in many of the same organizations. We were both on the board of the New England Surgical Society, and we both served eventually as its president. We were both directors of the American Board of Surgery. We each served as chief of surgery in our respective hospitals. And so on. These professional contacts deepened our friendship and gave us opportunities for social contacts as well as professional ones. On skiing excursions, Clem, a native of Maine and a truly expert skier, kindly abandoned the most challenging slopes to ski on less challenging trails with me. He also tried, with limited success, to improve my skiing technique. I still remember his admonitions to "keep your weight on the big toe of your downhill foot" and to "hug the big teddy bear downhill." When I could keep his tips in mind, my weight stayed in the right place and my body lined up correctly. Watching Clem closely and trying to copy his graceful turns was even more helpful. Seeing Clem ski effortlessly down a steep slope was a joy!

Clem had many character traits I admired, but the one I admired most was his commitment to bringing medical help to poor and needy people in far-away places. At his own expense, he would go anywhere he saw an opportunity to serve. After his third year in medical school, he spent a summer assisting a solo practitioner in Twillingate, a remote fishing village in northern New-foundland. He did a bit of everything there, including delivering babies. Those young mothers must have been grateful for his care and compassion. One of them named her newborn son for Clem.

Later, as a fully trained surgeon, Clem served on the *S.S. Hope*, a hospital ship that brings surgical procedures to poor patients in the third world. Clem also worked at the Albert Schweitzer Hospital in West Africa, and he greatly cherished a picture made there of himself and Dr. Schweitzer, the famous humanitarian, organist, philosopher, surgeon, and winner of the Nobel Peace Prize.

Clem had a special commitment to a remote part

of Brazil. He did remarkably challenging operations there under extremely difficult conditions and with surprisingly good outcomes. Clem somehow managed to bring a few patients to Maine for complex surgery and sometimes for postoperative recovery in his own home. I don't know how he handled the hospital costs; but I do know how resourceful, persuasive, and generous Clem was.

I share all this background about Clem so that you can understand how strong and capable and good-hearted my friend was, and what a loss it was to many people when Clem developed a severe case of Parkinson's disease. And what a shock and a profound sadness it was for me to watch the slow and inexorable loss of all those strengths I so admired in Clem, until finally there seemed to be nothing left of the man I had once been proud to call my friend. And what a shock it was that day when Dr. K said to me, "That's right! That's what you have … Parkinson's disease!"

I won't detail Clem's course, which was over ten years long. His wife, May, told me that the first five were "generally good years." She said, "The last five …." She didn't finish her description. A painful grimace conveyed her message. The last five years were increasingly awful. May kept Clem at home for as long as she could. Then he went to an assisted living residence. And then to a nursing home. And finally he needed total care.

Clem lost an incredible amount of weight but remained surprisingly strong. His mind, however, slowly slipped away. When I visited Clem during the last year or two of his life, I had no idea if he knew me. But I still felt compelled to visit.

One beautiful October day, I visited Clem when

the New England fall foliage was at its peak color. I was determined that Clem should see the fall colors one more year. With the nurse's permission and with some struggle, I strapped Clem into a wheelchair and pushed him out the front door of the nursing home. Bright sunlight highlighted the dramatic red of the maple trees and the vibrant yellow of the birches. I pushed his wheelchair along the sidewalk to the end of the block. From there, we could look out over a golf course. Its broad green fairways complemented the bright colors of the trees. For several minutes we just sat there. Clem's face was a mask, typical of late Parkinson's disease, totally devoid of any emotion. He said nothing, but his eyes fixed on the trees, moving occasionally from one to another. After what seemed a long time, we left the beautiful foliage, and I slowly wheeled him back to the nursing home. From that time on, I never saw him give any sign of being aware of his surroundings.

Several months later, after a long, slow, inexorable progression of his disease, there was little left of his body—and nothing left of his mind. Clem's physician met with May. He said simply, "I think it's time to let Clem go." May agreed. From her perspective, the Clem that she loved had gone a long time before. With her blessing, the physician wrote a medical order: "Comfort Care Only." It meant no forced feeding, no attempt to resuscitate, no antibiotics, no treatment of any kind except whatever would make Clem more comfortable. By that time the order was hardly necessary. Clem spent most of his time sleeping. He ate or drank little. Over a few days, he became less and less responsive. His breathing slowed down and became shallow. Finally, he just stopped breathing. It was a peaceful death, and a merciful one. Clem would have wished it had come much sooner.

I am determined that I will not die like he did. I hope that Dr. K was right and that I will live a long time with a mild form of Parkinson's and die of something totally unrelated. Perhaps heart disease, cancer, or stroke, the most common causes of death in our country. Or possibly a sudden and unexpected death from an automobile accident, a bad fall, or a heart attack. More likely than not, my death will be due to some other disease with a predictable and manageable course, one that will not be too distressing to me or my family. The chances of that are fairly good, I think.

But what if no other disease comes along to carry me off? What if I die of Parkinson's after all? Am I doomed to die like Clem, not knowing my friends or family? Can I prevent becoming an undue burden on them?

I believe that I can. I can live with physical disabilities that require the help of others. I have had brief experiences with needing help from others. When I ruptured my Achilles tendon playing tennis and later when I had two knee replacements, I required help for several weeks. I have spent much of my own life helping others: mainly patients, but also friends and family members. I have enjoyed helping them. Helping others can be a gratifying thing to do, rather than a burden. It can even be a privilege. Perhaps helping me can be gratifying to my caregivers. Perhaps I have something to learn from being helped. As long as my mind is clear and functioning well, I can enjoy talking to others and hopefully even contribute in some way to their welfare. I can enjoy reading, looking at art, and listening to music. I can still enjoy getting outdoors in the world of nature. I have known many patients with severe disabilities who had a good life despite their limitations. I believe that I can do the same.

But what if my mind starts to go, as it did with Clem, and as it does with many Parkinson's patients? That is my greatest fear. The first symptoms would probably be subtle and easily overlooked: misplacing things, becoming forgetful, trouble concentrating, slowed reaction times, and so on. These symptoms are common in older people and do not necessarily lead inexorably to dementia. How would I know when I am about to cross the line from normal aging to impending dementia? When would I realize that I was about to lose my mental acuity and that it would be irreversible? And if I do realize that loss of my mind is imminent, what is the best way to prevent becoming a burden for my loved ones? These are not easy questions to answer.

Suicide is an option, of course. However, I cannot imagine ever putting a loaded pistol to my head and pulling the trigger, as Dr. Francis Moore, my old chief, did. Or driving a car at high speed into a concrete bridge abutment. Or jumping off a bridge. Or any other violent means of ending my life, leaving painful memories for my family.

Suicide just seems wrong to me, even if the means are peaceful, such as a drug overdose. I have always felt that human life is precious, even sacred. To end my own life suddenly goes against my deepest convictions. Suicide is considered immoral by the world's great religions, and aiding a suicide victim is illegal in most countries. Especially troubling to me is the emotional pain and guilt that suicide inflicts on survivors. Much as I might wish to avoid the living death of dementia and the heavy burden it inflicts on families, it is hard for me to imagine ever committing suicide. Perhaps there is an appropriate time and place for suicide for some people, but I cannot make that case for myself.

On the other hand, dying on a respirator in an ICU when there is no reasonable hope of recovery seems equally wrong and unnatural to me. I have seen far too many patients die in the hospital on life support machines, even though their death was inevitable and treatment was futile. Those patients were denied a peaceful and dignified death, and their loved ones were inflicted with unnecessarily painful memories. I have often wished that terminally ill patients could somehow avoid having to suffer prolonged dementia or intractable pain without having to take their own lives. I would also like to spare them an aggressive but futile attempt to prolong their lives. I have hoped they could find a gentle and natural way to die. I have also hoped to find a gentle and natural way to die myself, if the Parkinson's disease progresses and dementia looms ahead.

I have wondered just what is a peaceful and "natural" way to die. I have wondered how animals die "naturally." There are many ways, of course. Some animals fall victim to predators. Others succumb to disease. When most animals are sick or injured, they seek out a secure and secluded spot to curl up and rest. They make no effort to eat or drink. A sick pet will usually refuse attempts to feed it. Fasting seems to be good treatment for many illnesses in both animals and people. The body seems to know when food is not needed. With life-threatening diseases, fasting often sets the stage for a quiet and peaceful death for the animal.

In primitive societies, something similar happens when a member of the tribe can no longer contribute to the group because of age or illness. These primitive tribes cannot afford to feed and care for those who will never again be able to care for themselves. Elderly or debilitated members of the tribe are led out into the forest or out over the tundra or out onto an ice floe. There they lie down and go to sleep with the hope that they will not wake up. Without food or water, their wish may come true before long. In cold climates, hypothermia often speeds a fatal outcome. Life in these primitive societies is harsh. It does not permit using the limited supply of food to feed those nearing death. Failure to provide food to those nearing death is not only necessary for the tribe, but it may also be a kindness to the dying. In our own society, it seems to me ethically appropriate for a terminally ill patient to refuse food or fluids, like a sick animal, and thereby hasten death.

I regard death of the mind as death of the person, even when the body can linger on in a vegetative state. To me, the worst death of all is death of the mind in a body that lives for a long time. When irreversible dementia seems inevitable, and when enough mental capacity remains to allow it, I believe that it is appropriate to stop eating and drinking. And I would not rule out taking narcotics or other medications that were given to relieve pain, provide comfort, and ease the dying process.

So how would my own death play out, if no other disease carries me off and I am fated to die of Parkinson's disease? As disability progresses, I would stay the course as long as I could. I feel that life has a purpose and that death may be its culmination. I would hate to check out early on what might be life's greatest lesson. I would learn what I could from dealing with disability and accepting the help of others; but I would watch closely for the approach of dementia. If I anticipate losing my mental capabilities before long, I would stop eating and drinking, except perhaps for sips of water or dissolving bits of ice in my mouth, as necessary for comfort. But before refusing food or fluids, I would go over the reasons for my decision with everyone affected by it: my family, my physician, my minister, and perhaps a few friends. I would like their understanding and support. I would also like to be sure that all my legal and financial affairs were in order, so I would check with my lawyer and my financial advisor.

I would seek hospice care early. When I was working with the largest hospice organization in Worcester, the most common complaint of families was: *Why didn't we get referred for hospice care sooner?* The average hospice stay was only about a week, not long enough to be too helpful. Hospice care can do a lot to help a dying patient live as fully as possible, for as long as possible. And it can be a godsend to the caregivers. Perhaps my worst fear is being a heavy burden to my family, especially my wife. So I would seek hospice help early. I would also explore the benefits of part-time or fulltime help in our home.

I would like to die at home. Betty and I moved into the house of our dreams in April of 2002. We hope to live in it for the rest of our lives. The house is a nine-room colonial that sits high on a rocky ledge overlooking the ocean. From the front windows of our home, we can see waves breaking on the rocks below us and on the islands of Casco Bay. We have a view of two lighthouses and ships sailing in and out of Portland Harbor. Lobstermen tend their pots, and fishermen tow their nets. In the summer we see sailboat races and cruise ships. Year-round we see oil tankers, freighters, and ferries to the islands. With the interplay of light, wind, clouds, and fog on the water, the scene is endlessly fascinating. I could watch that scene with contentment for the rest of my life.

While waiting for death to come, I would like the home environment to be pleasant and to include music and flowers. Most important, I would like to have Betty and other family members there. I would welcome a loving touch: holding a loved one's hand, having a Reiki treatment, or perhaps a massage. I would like to talk at length with my wife and family. I would enjoy listening to them read books or poems. I want to remain conscious and alert for as long as I can, but I would be glad to have a sleeping pill or a pain medication if needed. I would like to read (and re-read) good books, and perhaps look at family picture albums and re-live past travels and other highlights of my life. I would like to review my spiritual and religious beliefs, first in my own mind and then perhaps with others. It could be an exciting time, preparing for the start of a great adventure!

I would like to have a Walkman or iPod near so I could listen to music whenever I wished. Music was comforting to me when I had my knee replacements. I had been told to bring in a Walkman and some of my favorite tapes. The first day after surgery, it was helpful to cope with the pain when I was told to get up and walk, with only the support of a walker. The knee hurt—a lot.

After walking around the ward with a walker, the knee was throbbing and hurting more than ever. My surgeons suggested that I try to distract myself. Closing my eyes and listening to music was a big help. I found that different music matched different moods. Sometimes I felt like hearing blues or gospel tapes or Dave Bruback or the New Black Eagle Jazz Band. More often, I liked listening to the peaceful sounds of Gregorian chants, Bach partitas, Renaissance madrigals, or spiritual chants from the religious community at Taizé, France. It was good to have a diverse selection.

I expect to spend time meditating. I first began meditating in the early 1970s. I was under a good bit of stress then. I was chief of surgery at St. Vincent Hospital and supervising its residency program. At the same time, I was chair of the Department of Surgery at UMass Medical School. Both positions were full-time, at least in theory. I also had a surgical practice. At home I had a wife and four young children. Looking for an antidote to all the stress, I read an article about the benefits of TM, transcendental meditation, as popularized by Indian guru Maharishi Mahesh Yogi. I was especially impressed that two young Harvard research fellows, Keith Wallace and Herb Benson, had documented the ability of TM to slow the pulse and breathing, lower the blood pressure, and bring about favorable changes in blood chemistry. I decided to take the TM course.

Much of the Hindu imagery of TM felt alien and uncomfortable to me, but the meditation itself was a powerful anti-stress tool. For 20 minutes, the first thing each morning, usually in the dark, I silently repeated a mantra I had been given by the TM instructor, Bill

Deknatel. After returning home each evening, I repeated the same meditation. And it worked! Meditation was a powerful tool to neutralize the stress in my life. Later, I learned different forms of meditation from Jon Kabat-Zinn, Thich Nhat Hahn, Ram Das, Joseph Goldstein, and others. All methods serve to focus my attention on the present moment. Meditation is not necessarily religious, but every major religion has its own meditative practices. I believe that meditation will help to bring peace and comfort as I approach the end of my life.

At some point, I will need to say goodbye and withdraw my awareness to a place where my loved ones cannot join me. I hope that my withdrawal from them will be understood and respected, hopefully even inspiring. I have known some deaths that were truly awesome—uplifting and comforting to the survivors. I hope that my own death will have a positive effect on those left behind.

As death approaches at last, I expect that I will want to sleep more and more. I have observed this often in dying patients. It seems peaceful and natural to sleep at such times. Gradually, the sleep becomes deeper. At times the patient is hard to wake up. Often, there are chest secretions that the patient is unable to cough up, setting the stage for bacteria to grow and a terminal pneumonia, called the "old man's friend" by physicians of an earlier era.

Sleep deepens into coma. The breath stops for a few seconds and then resumes with a sigh. The times in which the patient does not breathe become longer. Finally, a time comes when breathing stops and does not start again. After sitting by the bedside for a while to make sure that breathing will not resume, the caretakers contact those not present and tell them that the patient has passed away, quite peacefully. Often, family members will continue to sit quietly with the oh-so-familiar body, now still at last. Such times can be awesome. They may bring comfort, relief, and healing to the survivors. They can be "good deaths."

No one can read the future, and no one can predict his or her own response to unforeseen circumstances. Perhaps my own death will be quite different from what I have seen and described. In particular, I realize that it may not be practical to care for me at home. I realize also that my wife may become sick or disabled or even die before I do.

I hope and expect to have a good death. But I know that a good death is more likely to happen, if planned well in advance with loved ones, long before a health-care crisis. Our family has begun that conversation. We re-visit it annually.

Life has many mysteries: The universe is a mystery. The human body is a mystery. Consciousness is a mystery. Where did they all come from? Why? I do not have the answers, but I am content with the mystery. All that I have experienced—and that I have tried to record in this book—has given me increasing comfort with the unknown. Whoever (or Whatever) created it all is much too big for me to comprehend. But I feel that behind it all, there is a Vast and Creative Consciousness. We might as well call it God. And it contains Beauty, Truth, and Love. Especially Love.

Death remains the ultimate mystery, but it is a mystery that I no longer find threatening. The door to whatever lies beyond death remains tightly closed, but I have seen cracks of light around it. When that door opens, I expect to step through with a sense of relief and anticipation. And I do not expect to be alone.

The great Indian poet Rabindranath Tagore, once wrote (to paraphrase), "Death is like snuffing out a candle … in the first light of dawn."

I hope—and believe—it is true!

EPILOGUE

The Death of Socrates

—

When I was a college freshman at Vanderbilt, I read *Plato's Republic*. The description of the death of Socrates had a powerful impact on me. That ancient philosopher's calm and clear-headed insights about dying have affected my attitude toward death ever since. So it seems appropriate to close this book with the story of how Socrates, the wisest man in the ancient world, approached his death.

—

In 399 B.C. the 70-year-old philosopher Socrates was put on trial for his life. The charge was that he did not believe in the gods and that his ideas were corrupting the youth of Athens. Socrates maintained that he had not corrupted the youth, but that Athens itself was corrupt. He angered his jurors, and he was sentenced to die by drinking poison hemlock.

When the fatal verdict was announced, Socrates was calm and composed. Plato wrote down his final words to the jury. In part, Socrates said: "Death is one of two things. Either it is a dreamless sleep from which the sleeper does not wake, in which case it is a permanent relief from the troubles of the world. Or else, as some say, there is a relocation of the consciousness to another realm, and perhaps the chance to question those who have died before, in which case what greater blessing can there be? It is time to depart…. For me, to die … for you, to live … but which of us is going to a better state is known only to God."

Socrates had thought deeply about many important issues in life, and he had also questioned others as to their beliefs before reaching his own conclusions. He had been a soldier in some bloody battles and must have encountered death many times. And now he was on trial for his own life. Surely he had thought deeply about death before giving his famous address to his jurors, and his conclusions gave him comfort when he was sentenced to die.

In the last book of Plato's *Republic*, Socrates recounts what would now be called a near-death experience. It is the story of Er, an Athenian soldier who suffered severe battle wounds and appeared to be dead. After 12 days, his body was placed on a funeral pyre. However, Er regained consciousness before the pyre was set ablaze. He then told his fellow soldiers a remarkable story. According to Socrates, Er said that during the time he appeared to be dead, he had gone in spirit form to a heavenlike hereafter. There he saw newly dead spirits being judged for deeds in their earthly lives. Other spirits were being prepared for rebirth into a new earthly life. Er was shown much more, but he was told that his time had not yet come to remain in the afterlife. He must return to Earth and tell people what he had seen.

Er's story was widely known in ancient Athens and generally regarded as true. Perhaps Socrates had Er in mind later when he was telling his jurors: "Some say there is a relocation of consciousness to another realm and perhaps the chance to question those who have died before." Plato leaves us with the impression that Socrates favored this belief, while recognizing other possibilities, including "a deep sleep from which the sleeper does not wake."

Socrates had close friends with him when he drank the poison. The 19th century French painter Jean Louis David depicted the scene described by Plato. His famous painting now hangs in the Metropolitan Museum of Art in New York. In the painting, Socrates appears not at all downcast, even though his followers are grieving deeply. He seems almost defiant as he reaches for the cup of poison, and he points upward as though to heaven. According to Plato, as his death drew near, Socrates spoke to his closest follower, Crito. His last words were, "I owe a cock to Asclepius. ... Will you pay the debt?"

When Socrates spoke these words, he was in the jaws of death. If there was ever a time for a deathbed vision or a prophetic insight, it was then. We'll never know if he had some heavenly vision, but at least Socrates had an insight into the meaning of his own death.

In ancient Greece, when a person recovered from a serious illness or injury, it was customary to make a gift to the Temple of Asclepius, the god of healing. One customary gift was a rooster. The rooster was chosen as a sacrificial animal for the god of healing because it is the symbol of the sunrise. The practice was to sacrifice the rooster with the very first rays of the rising sun. Simultaneously, the doors of the Temple of Asclepius were thrown open so that the first rays of the sun struck the statue of the god within. Asclepius was the son of Apollo, god of the sun.

The conventional interpretation of most scholars is that, face-to-face with death, Socrates saw death as a healing for which he should be grateful, and for which he should accordingly give thanks to Asclepius, the god of healing. Furthermore, they believe that he saw death as the dawn of a new day. A German classics professor wrote about the last words of Socrates as follows: "Scholars were long puzzled as to the meaning of Socrates' strange last words. ... Today we know what he meant. He might just as well have said: 'The sun is rising, the light is coming, let us give thanks.'" In other words, death looked to Socrates like the dawn of a new day.

From Plato, we know that although Socrates disclaimed any specific knowledge of what happens after death, he clearly favored the belief that "there is a relocation of consciousness to another realm." His convictions about death must have contributed to his composure when he was sentenced to die, as well as when he drank the poison hemlock.

How many of us ever think through our beliefs about death? It brings up many unpleasant associations. For many, death is the ultimate threat, the loss of everything. But sooner or later, we all have to face up to our own mortality. Doing so well in advance of a life-threatening illness can be a great comfort. Prior to writing this book, I had never sat down to think through my beliefs about death and an afterlife. However, both my personal life and my medical practice have been filled with experiences that have shaped my views about death. They have taken me from a childhood terror at the thought of death, to a place of comfort with death in my older years. Those experiences and the insights they provided are the substance of this book. I hope that they may be of interest, and perhaps some comfort, to my readers, just as they have been to me.

AFTERWORD

I Find My Life Partner

—

My wife, Betty, was a direct participant in some of the preceding stories and a firsthand observer of others. That is why this introduces the reader more fully to Elizabeth Jane Maxwell Wheeler of Portland, Maine.

In February of 1956, I was a surgical resident at the Peter Bent Brigham Hospital in Boston. One weekend, I decided to go skiing. Having grown up in the South, I was a beginner. I went to Cannon Mountain in New Hampshire, rented skis, boots, and poles, and took a rope tow to the top of the bunny slope. With every muscle stiff in an awkward attempt at a snowplow, I cautiously made it safely to the bottom of that gentle slope. I was exhilarated! Encouraged by initial success, I took a chair lift up a steeper slope. At the top, that slope looked alarmingly steeper than it had from the bottom looking up. It was clearly too much for me to handle. Cautiously, I started down in my stiff snowplow. In a few seconds, I was going much too fast. The skis raced out from under me and I went tumbling down the hill, landing with a crash on my ski poles.

To my great relief, my arms and legs were intact and working normally. I had no serious injuries, only a few tender spots. The ski poles didn't fare as well. They were bamboo, and I had slammed 200 pounds onto them with great force. One was splintered badly. The other was cracked. They were useless. I took off my skis and slowly made my way step-by-step down the slope, carrying the skis and poles. I went straight to the ski shop, where they rented me some aluminum poles. To my relief, they didn't charge me for the damage to the bamboo pair.

While I was talking to the shop manager about replacing my damaged ski poles, I noticed an attractive young woman in a dark ski parka standing off to one side. She was looking at me with obvious interest. I wondered who she was and why she was looking at me. After I got the new poles, I walked over to speak to her. Feeling a bit self-conscious, I asked, "Haven't we met?" I was embarrassed at how trite my words sounded.

"Yes, we have," she replied. "You once dated my good friend, Pat Preti. She and I shared an apartment on Commonwealth Avenue in Boston. We met there. Once we even went on a double date with Pat and a friend of yours."

Of course! How could I forget? Her roommate had been my steady date during medical school. But Pat and I came from different backgrounds, and we were different people in many ways. So we finally went our separate ways, but not before Pat once arranged a double date with her childhood friend Betty Maxwell and my fellow surgical intern Ray Kjellberg. Three years later, after being drafted by the U.S. Army and sent to Korea, I had returned to finish my surgical residency in Boston. That was how I came to be at Cannon Mountain. Betty had come to ski with friends. She had stopped skiing for lunch and put her skis in a rack outside the lodge. When she came back to the ski rack after eating, her skis were gone. Someone had taken them by mistake. So, she went to the ski shop to rent another pair. And there she saw me—and quickly remembered our double date of a few years before.

Betty spent the rest of her afternoon on the bunny slope with me, patiently teaching me how to ski. I was in awe of my kind, thoughtful, and lovely ski instructor. At the end of the afternoon, we arranged to get together again in Boston. That first date quickly led to others. Before long, I found myself wondering if Betty might be the life partner I had been looking for. Our interests and our values were strikingly similar, and I greatly respected her intelligence and common sense. Her candor and total lack of pretense was refreshing. I admired her keen interest in a wide variety of fields: from art to nature, from science to world religions. I was not surprised to learn that she taught science at Beaver Country Day School—a well-known private school. But my feelings toward Betty went beyond admiration and respect. She aroused other feelings as well. I was falling in love.

There was a big obstacle to enjoying a leisurely courtship. It was April. I was committed to leave for a year's surgical fellowship in London in July. I already had booked a single stateroom on a Cunard ocean liner, the *HMS Carinthia*, sailing the end of July from Montreal to Liverpool. Time was rapidly running out if I wanted to make wedding plans. Was I really ready to ask Betty to marry me, based on only a few dates? More to the point, would she be willing to marry me, based on the same few shared experiences? And was it still possible to get a reservation for two on the *Carinthia*?

I called a travel agent to see if I could get the ship reservation. To my relief, I was able to book a double stateroom. But I cautiously held onto the single reservation too, just in case Betty turned me down. About two weeks after I got the double reservation, we had a particularly nice evening together, ending up back at her apartment in Cambridge. The conversation turned to my upcoming transatlantic voyage. Betty seemed unusually subdued. Softly, slowly, timidly, I told her that I had made a reservation for a double stateroom and that I hoped—with all my heart—that she would come with me. Betty didn't say a word. She started to cry, but her tears were the tears of joy. We held each other close in silence for a long time. Nothing needed to be said. We were engaged. We were going to be married. We were going to live together for the rest of our lives. Several days later, Betty told me that if I had not asked her to marry me that night, she planned to tell me that she would never see me again. She said it would just have been too painful when I sailed away and left her behind.

Time was short. Plans moved quickly. I slipped an engagement ring onto Betty's finger a few days later, while we were standing beneath a massive oak tree near the Swan Boat pond in Boston Garden. We were married on July 21—my birthday—in an old, white New England church in Sebago Lake Village, Maine. Betty's family had a summer home there. She had spent many pleasant summers growing up on Sebago Lake. She wanted to add the crowning memory. And so we began a long and happy life together.

Betty has been an ideal partner in many diverse situations and adventures. In time, we had four children, with all the usual joys and concerns that children bring. We have traveled widely, with and without children, especially for mountain hiking trips. Betty has accompanied me on a 17-day trek in the Himalayas and a 12-day rafting trip through remote mountains and virgin forests in Alaska. We have canoed the Allagash River in northern Maine and the lake country of the Cree Indians in northern Canada.

Betty and me at the end of a 12-day rafting trip in Alaska

Family rafting trip, Arkansas River, Colorado, 1989

Together, Betty and I have enjoyed countless cultural events, including concerts, plays, and museum exhibitions. We have gone on Buddhist and Hindu spiritual retreats. Our interests and beliefs have changed over time. We have grown together.

And Betty can vouch personally for the validity of some strange events described in this book. She was an important partner in many of my most meaningful experiences.

ACKNOWLEDGEMENTS

—

This book is the product of many hands and hearts. Most of all, I wish to thank my wife and family for their constant support and helpful suggestions. My son, Stephen, is a professor at the University of California, Davis who has published several textbooks in the area of sustainable development and urban design. His wife, Mimi, is a professional editor. My daughter, Jane, is a medical writer who has helped launch the Meredith Winter Press. So I have been blessed with high-level advice from my own family.

I also received constructive advice and encouragement, early in the process of writing this book, from two friends: Frank Smith, a professional writer, and Humphrey Doermann, a retired foundation president and published author.

I would like to thank other early readers whose support was helpful including Colleen Sanders, Wes Bonney, Diane Smith, Priscilla Grant, Emily Coombs, Randy Matthews, Cristina Silari, Fred Anderson, Chris McClusky, Jeff Bernhard, and Joe Semmes. Additionally, I am grateful to Terri Grover, whose expert computer consulting helped me manage many drafts and a complex process, and to Joe Muir, who took old family photographs and 60-year-old school yearbooks and created publishable illustrations.

My special thanks to the team at Meredith Winter Press: David Kantor, Kenidi Kern, Jane Wheeler, Ceci Sorochin, Kathy Weflen, Alan Venable, and others I may not know, who turned a working draft into a publication of which I am proud. Many thanks to one and all.

My heartfelt thanks to the late Sherwin B. Nuland, MD. Shep urged me to write this book and called to encourage me after he read a draft. It meant a lot.

Finally, thanks to all those who made important contributions to this book but were inadvertently overlooked. And also to those whose names were mentioned, but who deserve much more than a brief mention. You and I both know who you are.